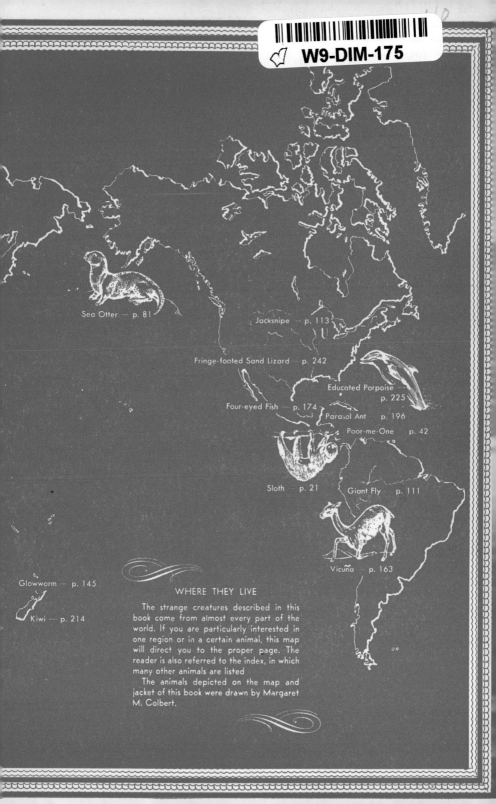

W9-DIM-175

Sea Otter — p. 81

Jacksnipe — p. 113

Fringe-footed Sand Lizard — p. 242

Educated Porpoise — p. 225

Four-eyed Fish — p. 174

Parasol Ant — p. 196

Poor-me-One — p. 42

Sloth — p. 21

Giant Fly — p. 111

Vicuña — p. 163

Glowworm — p. 145

Kiwi — p. 214

WHERE THEY LIVE

The strange creatures described in this book come from almost every part of the world. If you are particularly interested in one region or in a certain animal, this map will direct you to the proper page. The reader is also referred to the index, in which many other animals are listed

The animals depicted on the map and jacket of this book were drawn by Margaret M. Colbert.

Strangest Creatures

on Earth

This edition is especially
printed for the friends
of

Manufacturers
Santa Clara, California
U. S. A.

Pengo Auger	Pengo Cutting Heads	Pengo Bucket Cutter	Pengo Wisdom Teeth	Pengo Anchor Augers

Manufactured in U. S. A., England and Australia

New equipment for stringing overhead power line conductors under tension!

Stringing 336,400 CM aluminum conductor over energized lines with the new Pengo Tension Wire Stringer.

End view of Pengo Tension Wire Stringer showing multigrooved Bull wheels and wire reel rollers.

Gerald A. Petersen, inventor, explaining construction design details to an electrical engineer.

Pengo Duct Rodding Machine

Pengo Pole and Transformer Chariot

Pengo Flight Auger

Pengo Screw Anchor Tool

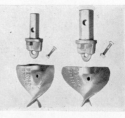

Pengo Pulling Eye

Pengo Screw Bit for Small Diameter Holes

PENGO "HOME" IN SUNNY CALIFORNIA!

PETERSEN Engineering Company office and manu-
facturing plant, Santa Clara, California, in the south
San Francisco Bay Area.

WHERE PENGO AUGERS ARE MANUFACTURED IN ENGLAND!

Lake and Elliott, Limited,
Braintree, Essex, have been
making quality steel cast-
ings for over half a century.

OFFICE OF PENGO IN AUSTRALIA!

Tutt-Bryant, Ltd., main office. Have branches throughout Australia. Manufacture
and distribute PENGO
Augers Nationally, in New
Zealand, and the surrounding islands.

Library of Congress Catalog Card Number: 53-7668

PUBLISHED SIMULTANEOUSLY IN CANADA
BY GEORGE J. MC LEOD, LTD., TORONTO, CANADA

MANUFACTURED IN THE UNITED STATES OF AMERICA

Strangest Creatu
on Earth

EDITED BY

EDWARD M. WEYER, JR.

Editor, Natural History Magazine

SHERIDAN HOUSE · NEW YOR

TO
FLEETWOOD STOLTZ
WHO CAN TELL THE TRUTH

SO IT SOUNDS LIKE A LIE

✤ CONTENTS ✤

7

8   *Contents*

FOREWORD

Some will say that it is presumptuous of anyone, with all Creation to choose from, to say, "Here are the strangest creatures on earth." Our choice cannot possibly suit everyone. In choosing these articles from *Natural History* Magazine, I have read about twenty million words, but I am ready to admit that there remain just as many animals that could be called just as strange. And some of the queerest have not yet found their biographer.

What makes a champion of strangeness? Peculiarity of form is surely enough sometimes. The giraffe is peculiar because it has a neck that is several times as long as anybody else's. And some of the strangest shaped animals are less well known and therefore more surprising. The African chameleon has a tongue that is longer than its whole body. Watch him use it in catching flies and you will admit that strangeness of behavior can make strangeness of form doubly astonishing. So too with the archer fish, which makes its living by shooting insects with a drop of water.

Many animals climb trees, but a fish that climbs trees is certainly strange. So is an animal that looks more like a flower than an animal. Most animals are strange because they are so different from ourselves, but the sea otter is strange because it acts so much like a person.

I believe it is good for us to look at these strange creatures, because there is so much pressure on us to look alike. This is the era of standardization. A century ago, almost everything in the home or office or on the farm had been made individually by hand. It was hard to find two objects just alike. Today, every object is stamped or molded in infinite similarity. One can scarcely find anything really singular outside a museum or in the unexplored world of nature.

9

If we took more time to enjoy the curious creatures with whom we share this planet, perhaps our political and social philosophy would grow healthier. It might help us to feel friendly toward the person who happens to be different from ourselves and to cultivate a regard for all of God's other creatures.

Note how ready the demagogue is to dress people alike— in a brown shirt or a black shirt—as a first step toward making them think and act alike. In the Age of Standardization, it will be our greatest problem to escape standardization of thought.

There will be less danger of it if we keep our senses and our hearts tuned to the living world around us. Nature is ever ready to exercise in us the unquenchable capacity for wonderment that must have stirred in man since the earliest times.

So for the moment, let yourself be bemused by the bizarre. Your imagination will be stretched. You will be carried beyond yourself. And if you pause to ask a single philosophical question at any point in this book, you will find yourself in the doorway to a vast new world of mysteries about the origin and development and destiny of a cosmos in which we ourselves can only have a small part.

Edward M. Weyer, Jr.
Editor

New York, N. Y.

Strangest Creatures

on Earth

❧ THE INCREDIBLE GIRAFFE ❧ *An Animated Watchtower that has difficulty coming down to earth for a drink* ❧ BY KEN STOTT, JR., GENERAL CURATOR, THE SAN DIEGO ZOO.

THEY stood browsing among the acacias, their spotted, sinuous necks arching above the trees. Gray tongues, wet and serpent-like, sought out the freshest, tenderest leaves and tore them from the branches. Tufted tails switched languidly from side to side. Even though my car was now only 200 yards from where these animated skyscrapers were stripping their lunch from the trees, they seemed entirely unaware of my presence.

The scene had an air of unreality about it, a stark sort of unreality that sprang, oddly enough, from familiarity. Although I had never laid eyes on the spot before, I knew it as well as my own street and number. It was a museum diorama come to life, and I had seen it in replica a hundred times before, as it waited eternally for the subtle touch of life.

Now, here before me, it breathed and moved and whispered—the golden infinity of Kenya's Athi Plains, the parasol-topped trees with their sparse, thorny foliage, the zebras, the wildebeests, the "Tommies," and—the giraffes!

The giraffes were hardest of all to accept as living flesh and blood. Yet there they stood, placidly munching away on acacia leaves with no inkling of the awe I felt.

Giraffes had long been favorites of mine in the San Diego Zoo, ever since, in fact, we had received our first pair in 1938. I had seen giraffes in circuses and other zoos before, but when our own zoo specimens emerged from the crates in which they had been shipped from Uganda, I felt certain that nowhere in creation could there be two more beautiful creatures than these, smudged and travel-weary though they were.

13

I marveled at their towering height and the fluid grace with which they glided in their pacing gait; at the quiet dignity with which they accepted the first uncertain ministrations of their new keeper; and perhaps most of all at the disarming, soul-searching quality of their gentle brown eyes. My reaction was an immediate attachment, and it is one from which I have never recovered. The novelty of having a pair of giraffes in our own zoo soon wore off, but the affection and interest I originally felt for them has grown, multiplying many times over with the birth of each new infant calf to the adult pair.

The same attachment, I found, held true for the wild giraffes in Africa. Unconfined by museum glass or zoo barricade, they were more amazing, more wonderful than ever.

The first group I saw was a small one, just inside the gate of Nairobi National Park on the Athi Plains. There were four of them: a bull, two cows, and a half-grown calf; and I came upon them while they were in the midst of their lunch (both figuratively and literally speaking). They fed from the crown of the same tree, spaced at intervals around it like any family foursome about the dinner table.

Behind them in the distance lay the outskirts of Nairobi itself, and only a few hundred yards away traffic bustled up and down the busy Magadi Highway. The proximity of civilization had little apparent effect on them. It was obvious that the protection they had enjoyed for a number of years had won their confidence to an astonishing degree.

As my car crawled toward them, they paused in their feeding from time to time, rearing their heads briefly before resuming their meal. Their curiosity was at first quite casual and only momentary. But as I drove closer, they watched more and fed less. Finally, with an air of, "Oh, well, we were through eating anyway," they sauntered off.

A short distance away, they stopped and turned and stood watching me. Patiently, they chewed their cuds and awaited

my departure with a concern that was due more to annoyance
than to fright.

As often as possible during my stay in the Nairobi area, I
drove out to the Park, which, conveniently enough, is situated
only a few minutes from the center of town. On each occasion,
I found the same giraffe family, and they were never far from
the acacia clump near the park entrance. That first meal was
not the only one I interrupted, but sometimes my visits were
more conveniently timed. I often saw them in the open, half
asleep and drinking-in the morning sun, and sometimes I came
upon them standing in the road.

Fortunately both for them and for the motorists, the speed
limit in the sanctuary is fifteen miles an hour, a pace that gives
the giraffes ample time to make a graceful exit. On the open
highway where speed is unlimited, giraffes constitute a considerable hazard, particularly at night.

I was to see many giraffe herds during the ensuing weeks,
but I never came upon a group without experiencing that initial reaction of combined awe and incredulity. I am still almost
ready to agree with the man who insisted, "There ain't no sech
animal!"

The giraffe observations and notes I had opportunity to
record in Africa could in no way be construed as scientific
studies. But in reviewing them, I find that, sifted and unscram-
bled, organized and digested, they do perhaps provide a key
to the character and behavior of this unique creation of nature.
Certain traits, I find, are referred to over and over again, so
repeatedly in fact that one cannot help drawing certain general conclusions. And of these traits, the giraffe's *laissez-faire*
approach to living tops the list.

There exists no less offensive a beast than the giraffe. It
lives peaceably with its kind for the most part and bears not
the slightest degree of ill-will toward other kinds of animals—
both of which, as character recommendations, are more than

can be said about the majority of people! Yet despite such in-
offensiveness (or perhaps because of it), the lofty giraffe is
sometimes an underdog. Because of its size, its enemies are
naturally few in kind, but what they lack in variety they make
up for in violence—and Man heads the list.

For some unaccountable reason, the giraffe is a favorite of
trophy hunters. Its head, stuffed with papier-mâché and a pair
of glassy, expressionless eyes, decorates many a sportsman's
den—and I use the word "sportsman" loosely, since walking up
to a giraffe in the field and dropping it in its tracks must in-
volve all the excitement and danger of bagging a Jersey heifer
in a dairy yard.

Both the lion and the leopard occasionally kill giraffes, but
they do it merely to appease their hunger. A single giraffe can
provide a hearty meal for an entire pride of lions as well as the
jackals, hyenas, and vultures that move in as soon as the big
cats have eaten their fill.

A giraffe has no means of defense unless, as one zoo worker
put it, you say it is the only animal that can kick in all four
directions at the same time. While this statement is a slight
exaggeration, it is nonetheless true that anyone working with
a giraffe in captivity had best keep an eye on its hoofs or he is
likely to be reminded of them in a most disconcerting manner.
In the wild, a hunter never gets close enough to a giraffe to be
in a position to worry about being kicked.

The giraffe's horns, small, knob-tipped and hair-covered,
are of little value in defending their bearer against predators.
To my knowledge, the only use to which they are put is in
the occasional combats that occur between two males. At such
times, one male lowers his head and shoves his horns between
the forelegs of the other. Then, with a mighty heave, he rears
his head, attempting to throw his adversary back on his
haunches.

The long neck of the giraffe, incredible though the conten-
tion may seem, contains exactly the same number of vertebrae

that grace the human neck. There are seven of them, but the degree of their elongation is without equal, and they serve their bearer in good stead.

The giraffe's neck constitutes a watchtower. This, combined with excellent vision and a good sense of smell, enables the animal to observe potential danger from a considerable distance. Unfortunately, the giraffe's judgment as to what constitutes potential danger and what does not is poor. Being cursed with an innate and irrepressible curiosity, the giraffe is often attracted by something that should scare the living daylights out of it.

This foolhardy characteristic is particularly evident in young animals. I have watched a mother giraffe pace excitedly back and forth while her precious calf edged closer, step by step, to where I stood motionless. No amount of snorting or head tossing by the alarmed parent had the slightest effect on the youngster, and only some slight but sudden movement on my part sent it rocking home to mother.

Among the most remarkable habits ascribed to the giraffe is that of the communal nursery. Some authors discredit the story entirely, describing it smugly as an old wives' tale. However, I have seen a single, mature giraffe cow surrounded by as many as nine youngsters, all under a year old—with not another adult giraffe within a mile in any direction. The gestation period of a giraffe is approximately fifteen months, and only one calf is customarily born at a time—never more than two. Since "novemtuplets" would be entirely out of the question, the only explanation I can offer for such an aggregation is the communal nursery theory.

Giraffes are generally sociable animals, with only an occasional misfit who appears to live alone and like it. Giraffe herds may include anywhere from half a dozen individuals to a hundred. The largest herd I observed consisted of approximately seventy members.

This group was led by a magnificent, black-spotted bull.

His neck was thick and muscular, and his forehead bulged with the protuberances that characterize most mature giraffe bulls. There were several other bulls in the herd but not one that even began to rival him in height, bulk, or coloration.

Yet impressive though this monster was, he was still not the most noteworthy member of the herd. That distinction belonged beyond doubt to a small and rather puny individual.

It was an albino, with reddish and poorly defined spots and interspaces of dusty white. Because of its poor vision, the albino always sought the center of the herd, apparently depending upon the behavior of the other animals to warn it when danger was imminent. Try as I might, I could not approach it closely enough to obtain a satisfactory picture. Invariably it was surrounded, and sometimes completely hidden, by its herdmates.

The herd permitted me to walk to within 300 or 400 feet of its outermost member. At this distance, however, the entire group began to move away. The retreat was executed not hurriedly, not nervously, but with a leisurely dignity. Only the leader remained steadfast, standing broadside and outlined against the sky like a massive statue. Finally, when he appeared to be satisfied that his compatriots had retreated to a safe distance, he too walked sedately away, serving as rear guard.

Giraffes are strictly browsing animals, feeding from the tops of acacias and other trees and shrubs of a convenient height. Their table manners are beyond reproach and quite in keeping with the graceful behavior that generally characterizes them. Drinking, however, is another matter.

When a giraffe drinks, it is forced to toss both grace and caution to the winds. In lowering its head to the water level, it becomes the ultimate in awkwardness. Sometimes it spreads its forelegs, stiffly and straight, at right angles to one another, and shifts its front feet farther and farther apart in shuddering jerks until at last it can reach the water. At other times it places the feet slightly ahead of the body and bends its forelegs forward and down, spider fashion, until the head is low enough to reach the water. In either case, the process is a slow and uncertain one. And once the animal's thirst is slaked, the recovery of its normal standing position is just as awkward.

Consequently, the giraffe is understandably reluctant to visit the water hole and does so only when it is absolutely certain that no danger lurks near by. If some strange scent disturbs the giraffe as it approaches the water hole, it refuses to drink until the scent is gone or its thirst becomes unbearable. It subsists in the meantime on what scant fluids it can glean from its food. Like the camel, the giraffe has been accredited with remarkable powers of abstinence. It can forego drinking for 40 or 50 days, or so the story goes! Such reports come under the heading of gross exaggeration, but it is safe to say that the giraffe may, and often does, go several days without water.

Of all the myths concerning the giraffe, the one most commonly repeated and most widely believed is that the creature is mute—that it lacks any vestige of vocal equipment. This is far from the truth, for the giraffe does have a larynx—a poorly developed and seldom utilized one, to be sure—but still a larynx. So far as I know, there are no authoritative reports of the vocalizing efforts of wild giraffes, but zoo specimens have been heard to "moo" softly. Thus, as Mr. George G. Goodwin of the American Museum has been quoted as saying, the giraffe is not mute, it is merely reticent.

There are several easily distinguishable types of giraffe. There is the Masai giraffe, with its brown maple-leaf blotches against a background of beige. Then there is the reticulated or Somali giraffe, with its red coat and network of immaculate white. And the Uganda giraffe has three bony protuberances in addition to the two bonafide horns, which have caused it to become known as the "five-horned" giraffe. Each of these and half a dozen other described forms have some individual claim for physical distinction. But whether the various forms are merely local races or constitute valid species is a matter worthy of considerable research.

The problem, however, is one that concerns only the taxonomist. As far as the African tourist is concerned, a giraffe is a giraffe, and nothing else matters. Here stands a creature that symbolizes Africa perhaps more than any other of the Dark Continent's magnificent animals. Nothing like it roams any other part of the world. It is and has been, throughout historic times, confined to Africa.

The late Martin Johnson, in selecting a color scheme for one of his amphibious planes, chose a giraffe-hide pattern. The choice was not the result of a mere whim. The plane was to be christened "The Spirit of Africa," and what design could be more appropriate than that of the giraffe!

LIVING UPSIDE-DOWN *The sloths, marvels of survival through stupidity and slowness*
BY WILLIAM E. LUNDY.

TWO WEEKS in the tropics was far too short a time to prepare my bride for the sight of the first "pet" I brought to her while we were living on the Panama-Costa Rica border. Standing some feet away, she gazed in astonishment at a sloth with long brownish-gray hair, which was hanging upside down from the seat of my railroad scooter.

An area of short, orange-colored hair on its back, encircling a black stripe along the spine—the so-called saddle mark—indicated that it was a male of the Three-toed species, so named because of the three claws on each of its feet.

The sloth's eight- or nine-pound body, with long forelimbs and short hind limbs, was suspended by twelve curved claws, three inches long, which held with a viselike grip. The claws seemed to grow from its ankles, for the soles of its feet were completely covered with long hair.

A mere stub of a tail and almost no semblance of a head made its long neck look longer, while the face appeared as only a splotch near the end. Small dull eyes, utterly devoid of expression, a small nose, and only a slit for a mouth combined to form the most idiotic face to be found on a mammal. Swaying slowly back and forth on the much-too-long neck, the eyes stared vacantly at nothing, while a hissing sound came almost continuously from its mouth.

My wife's look of astonishment turned to revulsion when she saw what appeared to be parasitic flies, disturbed by my handling of the sloth, working their way back into the long, coarse hair. As a seasick look played around her mouth, I realized that the joke had been carried far enough.

21

With a neighbor's help—for it is more than a one-man job
—I pried loose the long claws and placed the sloth on the
ground near a tree.

A sloth on the ground is a pitiful sight. Its shoulders appear
to be out of joint, for the limbs cannot support the weight of
the body when the animal tries to walk as other four-footed
mammals do. It is forced to drag itself along, belly scraping the
ground.

When it reached the tree, the sloth began to climb slowly.
Reaching a limb, the creature advanced along it, body hanging
underneath, suspended by the long claws of all four feet. So
slowly did it take each step, so deliberately did it hook each
set of claws over the limb, that one would have thought it was
stalking something rather than traveling its natural highway
back to the jungle and freedom. There, the contrast was remarkable. Gone was the crippled appearance; though still very
slow, the sloth was now master of its movements.

So strange is the appearance of these animals and so unique
their habit of walking upside down through the treetops that
explorers and naturalists have, over a period of four centuries,
written reams of fiction about them. Fortunately, a number of
scientists also have been interested in these strangely aberrant
mammals. Three, George B. Wislocki, Curt P. Richter, and
Robert K. Enders spent months on Barro Colorado Island, in
the Canal Zone, studying large numbers of sloths, and they
have recorded many interesting facts. Yet no description, including my own, can give an adequate picture of the sloths in
their native haunts.

Some local residents are unaware that another species, the
Two-toed Sloth (*Choloepus hoffmanni* Peters), is not uncommon here, though possibly outnumbered five to one by the
Three-toed (*Bradypus griseus griseus* Gray). Too many authors have seen specimens of only one species and in writing
their impressions have used the general term "sloth." One who

knows only a single species would consider a description of the other grossly inaccurate.

From a distance, you might easily mistake one kind for the other. At close range, however, many differences in looks and actions will be quickly noticed.

In sharp contrast to my wife's "pet," the Two-toed Sloth's face *does* show animation when disturbed, and its normal-sized eyes *will* focus on its enemies. A large bare nose, ending in wide nostrils, covers a mouth that is quite large when opened. It has no tail, no hair on the soles of its feet, and only two claws on its front feet. The limbs are of almost equal length.

While sleeping, rolled into balls with their necks tucked in between the forelimbs, sloths look more like inanimate objects than living animals. The Three-toed, squatting in a crotch, looks like a termite- or wasp-nest. The Two-toed, suspended among vines, becomes a half-hidden bird's nest or just a bunch of dried leaves.

During the dry season, when foliage is less dense, I vie with my wife in "spotting" sloths along the old Chiva-Chiva Road, some ten miles from Panama City. Once when she saw one, I contended that it was a termite nest until she announced triumphantly, "There, your termite nest is scratching its side!"

To Margorie Allee, one looked like "a dirty, shaggy door-mat." A visitor from the States once asked, "What is that old mophead doing in the crotch of that tree?" I once climbed to investigate a bird's nest—only to have it produce arms and legs and move slowly away through the vines. Yes, many people have seen sloths without knowing it.

Because he and his men had never seen sloths eat anything, Oviedo, the first chronicler of the Indies, wrote in 1535, "I could never perceive but that they live only of air." This idea must have been short-lived, for the sloth is a notorious glutton.

The Three-toed lives almost exclusively on leaves of the

Cecropia tree, locally known as *Guaruma*. This is the principal food of the Two-toed also, though in captivity it will eat
bananas and various vegetables.

A Three-toed Sloth may be handled with safety by grasping it from behind in the armpits. Its efforts at self-defense, to
quote William Beebe, can be circumvented by any creature
except another sloth. The lethargy of this species, attributed
by many writers to sloths in general, is far from true of the
Two-toed. One that I captured recently struck out furiously
whenever I came near. Their sharp, sickle-like claws can inflict
serious wounds.

A bit of Spanish humor is shown in the account of the sloth
written by Oviedo. He says, "The sloth is one of the slowest
beasts in the world, and . . . can scarcely go fifty paces in a
whole day." He then tells that they nicknamed it Perico Ligero
("Nimble Peter"), a name still used by many of the natives
today. Others call it Perezoso ("Lazy").

Sloths are so slow in their movements when undisturbed
that there is no need to exaggerate, yet many writers have done
so. Dampier told that before they could come down from one
tree and climb another, they were skin and bones, though they
were fat when they started, and that it took eight or nine minutes for them to move one leg forward three inches. Dr. Beebe
claims that "In action, the second hand of a watch often covers
more distance."

When approaching the trunk of a tree, suspended beneath
a horizontal limb, a Three-toed Sloth must do a rightabout-face
in order to descend, for unlike Dracula, it backs down. Only a
movie could adequately describe the process. Holding with the
forefeet, the animal unhooks the hind feet; and the rear end,
still on a level with the head, describes a half circle very, very
slowly. The sloth then proceeds backward down the trunk.

I have never witnessed a fight between sloths in the wild,
nor have I heard of such an encounter. It is well known, how-

ever, that placing two females in a cage together will often start a fight, which may end in death if they are not separated. Wounds are inflicted both with teeth and claws.

The Two-toed Sloth that I captured would repeatedly snatch a stick with which it was touched and bite it savagely with the canine teeth. Yet sloths have been classified under the order Edentata—or toothless!—and Oviedo said, "They bite not, nor can they bite, having very little mouths."

An incredible thing about the sloths is their ability to swim. These creatures, which have become so highly specialized for arboreal life that their feet are reduced to mere hooks for grasping, would seem to be the least likely to have this art. That sloths *can* swim has been known for nearly a century, for it was mentioned by Henry Bates in his *The Naturalist on the Amazons*. Others tell of sloths swimming rivers a mile or more in width.

Dr. Beebe called the sloth a "languidly loving creature," because two courtships he watched in Guiana resulted, as he put it, in nothing more serious than his own amusement. Perhaps the sloths of the Canal Zone take their love-making more seriously, for one love affair witnessed by Dr. Robert Enders lasted "from time to time over a period of two days"—and might have continued for an even longer period but for the accidental death of the "swain." Furthermore, he states that in a group of sloths that he bought, the "females . . . either had babies with them or were pregnant or both."

Baby sloths are born singly. These small balls of hair cling to the mother's chest, their tiny claws entwined in her long, coarse hair. In this way they are carried about until they are able to shift for themselves.

The Three-toed Sloth's defense of its young is little more effective than its self-defense—a slow swinging sweep of the forearms. When separated from her baby, the mother Three-toed apparently soon forgets it and goes about her business undisturbed. This is not so with the Two-toed mother, which fights viciously to protect the young. Some claim that she will destroy the baby rather than have it taken from her. Perhaps this does not occur intentionally but rather as a result of her savage efforts to defend it.

During the rainy season, when the jungle is greenest, multitudes of tiny green algae grow on the hair of the Three-toed Sloth, giving it a green sheen which makes the creature less conspicuous in the trees. Here, then, is a vegetable parasite that is of direct benefit to its animal host. Indeed, we should not call the alga a parasite but a partner.

Small moths are often found in large numbers in the hair of our sloths. It was some of these that my wife mistook for parasitic flies on her "pet." They have been observed to take moisture from the eyes and nostrils of a Two-toed captive. Local entomologists have combed the hair of many moth-infested sloths, searching in vain for the larvae, which have apparently not yet been recognized locally.

Almost unbelievable are some of the stories told of the tenacity with which these lowly mammals cling to life—recovery after suppression of respiration for 30 minutes by ether, recovery after 40 minutes of immersion in water, and survival for 30 hours after decerebration. "Of all animals," wrote Charles Waterton, "not even the toad or tortoise excepted, this poor ill-formed creature is the most tenacious of life. It exists long after it has received wounds which would have destroyed any other animal; and it may be said, on seeing a mortally wounded sloth, that life disputes with death every inch of flesh in its body. . . . I saw the heart of one beat for half an hour after it was taken out of the body." He told, however, that one sloth died in ten minutes, apparently without pain, after having been shot in a leg with an arrow that had been dipped in "Wourali" poison, a concoction made by the Indians of South America.

If records meant anything to a sloth, this strange creature

could boast of at least two. Of all mammals, it has the highest number of neck vertebrae, varying from six to nine instead of the usual seven.[1] It also has the lowest and most variable body temperature. From a low of 75 degrees F., it ranges to as high as 91 degrees. Even its "normal" temperature fluctuates between 85 and 91 degrees, according to Dr. Curt P. Richter.

It would have been strange indeed had no myths developed around a creature so weird in appearance and so unique in habits.

The lassitude of the sloth was believed by the early Spaniards to be due to heart trouble, which they thought the animal attempted to cure by scratching over the heart with the claws of the left hand, ". . . and thus the claw is the approved remedy against this evil."

According to one of the Spanish friars, "He who eats of the flesh of the perico ligero dies of it; because it is so phlegmatic." This myth may have influenced the natives of this section, for I have never heard of them eating one of these animals. This belief has probably helped considerably to ensure the sloth's survival in fair numbers in the Canal Zone. When the Indians of the Darien region of Panama saw one being prepared for Dr. Thomas Barbour's supper, they told him that the flesh of the sloth was unfit for food. It is well known, however, that many of the Indians of South America consider it a delicacy.

The Three-toed Sloth has been given credit for making a noise that belongs to another creature. I refer to a jungle voice that is so expressive of human sorrow that it has often been mistaken for a woman calling in hopeless grief. The myth that the sloth is the author of this cry has been prevalent for over

---

[1] Even the giraffe has only seven vertebrae in the neck, and exceptions to this number are rare among the mammals. The manatees have six, and the sloths have six, eight, or nine. The Little Anteater (*Tamandua*) has been said to have eight, and pangolins (of the genus *Manis*) may have eight, according to Flower and Lydekker (1891). In certain whales, the majority of porpoises, and some rodents, the neck bones are more or less united, and in the Right Whale they form a single bony mass. Some horses also do not invariably have seven, especially the Arabian horse.

four centuries; but we now know that it is made by a night-
bird of the goatsucker group (*Nyctibius griseus*).[2]

Another myth, which comes from Dutch Guiana, is that
one may not shoot a sloth, for should he do so, his gun would
be ruined.

Many who have seen the ungainly Three-toed Sloths in our
Canal Zone jungles are surprised that there *is* such an animal
today. Remembering all that they have heard of the constant
struggle for existence and the theory of the survival of the fit-
test, they marvel that a creature so slow, so stupid, and seemingly so unfit to cope with the many predators of a tropical
jungle could have survived. Yet survive it has, while the mighty
ground sloths which once inhabited this area are known only
by fossil remains.

Probably its survival is due to a combination of many
factors, foremost of which could well be protective coloration
and its habit of feeding mostly at night and remaining motionless during most of the day. Its 23 pairs of ribs, heavy coating
of fur and hair, and thick, tough skin all tend to protect the
viscera from claws and talons of predators, while its extreme
tenacity of life gives Nature time to repair wounds.

To those familiar with sloths in the wild, it is evident that
Count de Buffon's observations were limited to animals on the
ground. "The inertia of this animal," he wrote, "is not so much
due to laziness as to wretchedness . . . Inactivity, stupidity,
and even habitual suffering result from its strange and ill-
constructed conformation . . . Its only safety is in flight . . .
Everything about it . . . proclaims it to be one of those defective monsters, those imperfect sketches . . . which, having
scarcely the faculty of existence, could only continue for a
short time . . . They are the last possible term amongst
creatures of the flesh and blood, and any further defect would
have made their existence impossible."

At the other extreme we have the statement of Major R. W.

[2] See *Poor-me-One*, by William E. Lundy, page 42 of this book—Ed.

Hinkston that "No animal is better adapted than the sloth to a life in this virgin forest."

Perhaps their extreme specialization for life in the jungles will eventually work their downfall, for man is fast encroaching on the tropical forests, and to the extent that he does so, the domain of the sloth shrinks.

Unless large tracts of jungle lands are set aside for the preservation of wildlife, as was done on Barro Colorado Island in the Canal Zone, not many more generations of men will see these creatures walking upside down through their habitat. As Buffon expressed it, "They will be erased from the catalogue of living things."

DIVING SPIDERS *Indian spiders that prey upon fishes, run, float, and dive under water* BY GOPAL CHANDRA BHATTACHARYA, BOSE RESEARCH INSTITUTE, CALCUTTA, INDIA.

FAMILIAR with the rapid manner in which spiders move on land and with their web-spinning maneuvers in the air, many people do not realize that certain varieties have also attained astonishing mastery in the realm of water. To see them leap here and there on the surface of a river or lake is in itself a surprising sight, but most fascinating of all, perhaps, is their habit of submerging and remaining under water for considerable periods. Some are able even to prey upon small fishes.

A spider of this sort is *Lycosa annandalai,* whose activities it has been my fortune to observe in the neighborhood of Calcutta. I came across the specimens I am about to describe quite unexpectedly.

I was strolling through the suburbs of Calcutta in the month of March when I came upon a stagnant pool. Though the center was quite clear of weeds, its shores were completely overgrown with aquatic plants and grasses of various kinds. Around the edges the big green leaves of the Colocasia drooped over the surface of the water. These plants were the abode of another variety of spiders, the red-brown and spotted black stick-spiders of the genus *Tetragnatha.*

These spiders, with the purpose of preying upon various minute insects that hover or walk upon the surface of the water, attach themselves to the leaves, stems, or stalks of the Colocasia, where they may easily be mistaken for dead sticks.

I was trying, in vain, to capture some of these interesting creatures when my attention was drawn to a well developed stick-spider, which was passing from one plant to another. As the water was only knee-deep, I tried to catch it, but as I reached out, the spider, detecting danger, leaped with great alacrity upon the surface of the water. Immediately a big gray spider, with spotted back, came running from an adjacent leaf of Nymphoides (*Limnanthemum nymphoides*) and jumped upon the poor creature in the twinkling of an eye. The victim struggled, only to expire within a minute and a half. The aggressor then dragged the dead animal to a blade of grass and began feeding on it.

I resolved to capture the creature that had made the attack. But as I approached, it jumped and ran away; and I eventually lost sight of it entirely among the grasses that stood out of the water. I splashed the water and disturbed the vegetation sufficiently to cause several others of different sizes and shapes to come out on the surface of the water. Greatly alarmed, they began to run hither and thither.

I singled out another specimen and pursued it relentlessly. Soon the creature became tired and ran no more, but folded all its legs and crumpled itself into a mere mass, resembling something dead. This black mass was floating in an inverted position on the water by the side of some Nymphoid leaves. The instant I placed my fingers on it to pick it up, to my utter surprise it disappeared suddenly and completely, where, I could not follow. I had been quite close upon the creature, but I could not detect the secret of its escape.

For perhaps a quarter of an hour I searched in vain. Thoroughly disappointed, I was about to give up the chase when suddenly just to my right, I saw a big spider emerge from beneath the water. The mystery of their hiding themselves so quickly was then solved. This large specimen with grayish-black back and bluish-white lines around the cephalothorax, had been lurking below the surface. I had had no idea that these spiders could dive under water, like otters and beavers. Since discovering this, I have scarcely ever failed in capturing them.

When frightened, they suddenly submerge and remain clinging to the aquatic plants; and I have often seen them stay below for more than twenty minutes. Because of an air film surrounding their bodies, they look silvery white under water. The coating of air prevents the water from moistening them. The mother spider, carrying a cocoon from which young will eventually emerge, dives under water in a similar manner and under similar circumstances.

The depth to which the spider dives is usually several inches, and if pursued, it creeps for a considerable distance under water along the aquatic plants and tries to hide itself in a place of safety. When exhausted and unsuccessful at concealing itself, it feigns death, folding all its legs and floating on the surface of the water in an inverted position.

In some respects, both the males and females are of similar habits and frequent the same places. But the males keep at a safe distance from the females, lest they be attacked by them. Though smaller in size, the males are more formidable looking and run more swiftly than the females.

In the breeding season, the male idles here and there over the leaves or stalks of plants and grasses, or in bushes in search of a mate, while the female sits quietly under a bush or upon a leaf. When a male meets a female, both remain stationary for some time. If the female moves, the male follows her, keeping at a safe distance. If the female faces about, the male remains motionless as if dead. Presently the real courting begins and the entire operation takes a considerable time.

The observations I shall recount began about eight o'clock one morning at the edge of a stagnant pool at Kankurgachhi near Calcutta. I was squatting on a moist patch of land, when my attention was drawn to a small slender spider, which was moving in a peculiar dancing manner, repeatedly entering and leaving a small clump of aquatic plants and sometimes encircling the spot. It was not until later that I learned that his intended mate was lurking there. The male would advance

Africa's animated watch tower, the Giraffe, lives peaceably with its kind. Its gentle brown eyes sometimes cause people to forget that it can "kick in all directions at once."

(*See page 13.*)

Photo by George H. Her

There is no lethargy in the Two-toed Sloth's defense. This one lunged at the author with remarkable speed.

(*See page 21.*)

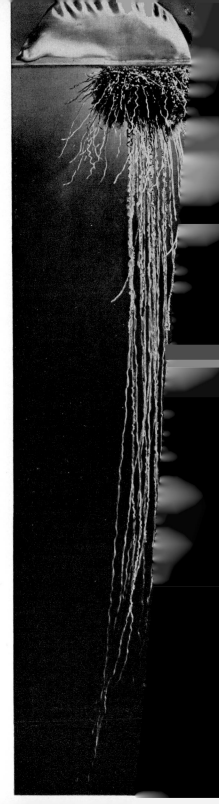

The Portuguese Man-of-War
is buoyed on the surface of the
sea by a translucent blue float
and sometimes sinks and rises
again. Great numbers are sometimes seen together, traveling
with the wind and current. A
certain little fish can swim safely
among the tentacles, but a bather
is instantly stung by thousands
of poisonous nettle cells.

(*See page 36.*)

Most horrible and ghostly is the cry of Poor-me-One, *Nycti-bius griseus*. For centuries explorers wondered what creature could possibly make so human and soul-stirring a song.

(*See page* 42.)

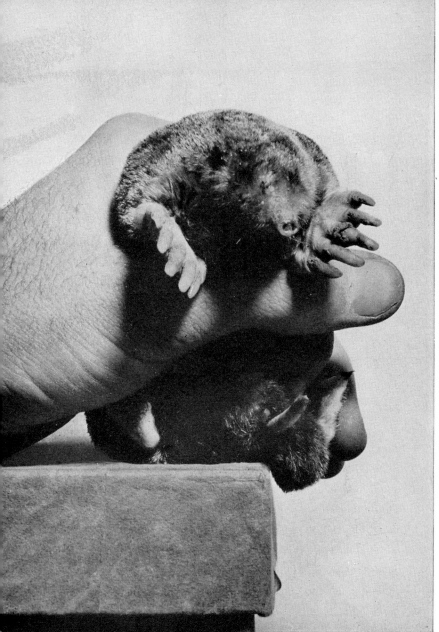

McHugh photo

The mole, nature's little "sand hog," depends on broad flat forefeet and strong claws. His eyes are almost useless. Kathryn and Byron Jackson have interpreted him as saying ". . . night or day, rain or shine, it's all the same in a life like mine."

(*See page 50.*)

Photo by James P. Chapin

A cocoon the size of a football might be expected to produce a moth the size of a rooster. But this is a "communal" cocoon and may yield as many as 300 or 400 moths.

(*See page 56.*)

A tail that is longer than the body does not prevent the Dusky Glider from being one of the greatest gliders among wingless animals. The crinkled edge of its flying membrane is visible. In flight, this is stretched between the elbow and the ankle on each side. This is a partly white specimen.

(*See page 58.*)

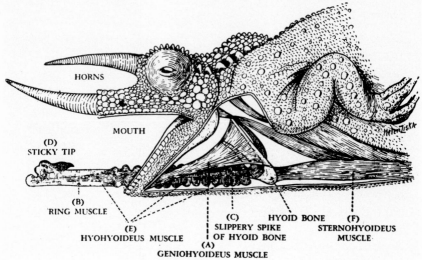

HORNS

MOUTH

(D)
STICKY TIP

(B)
RING MUSCLE

(E)
HYOHYOIDEUS MUSCLE

(C)
SLIPPERY SPIKE
OF HYOID BONE

HYOID BONE

(A)
GENIOHYOIDEUS MUSCLE

(F)
STERNOHYOIDEUS
MUSCLE

Drawing by Helen Ziska based on a dissection by H. C. Raven

The tongue of the chameleon is projected from the mouth in somewhat the same way that a watermelon seed can be shot from between the fingers. The tapering, slippery bone (C) inside the powerful muscles of the tongue might be called the exclusive feature of the chameleon's remarkable invention; the other muscles and bone differ from our own only in detail.

The chameleon projects its tongue as follows: It opens its mouth and draws the whole tongue apparatus forward like a gun on its carriage by contraction of muscle (A). After careful aim, the powerful ring muscle (B) contracts suddenly on the slippery spike-like bone (C), shooting the tongue forward on its rapid journey, which has just begun in this drawing. Extremely elastic, the tongue projects to great length.

The insect, if struck, adheres to the sticky tip (D); the tongue is then withdrawn by contraction of the elastic tissue and the "accordion pleated" muscle (E); and the muscle (F) pull the "gun carriage" into the back of the mouth.

Three horns, two of which show here, distinguish this chameleon from others, but the tongue mechanism is essentially the same.

toward the spot with very slow and cautious steps, counting paces as it were. He would raise his body to the maximum height and lower it again with a graceful movement of the pedipalpi, paying as it were homage to her majesty, with his head bowed down and both the pedipalpi folded. The pedipalpi were prominent and black, with femur and patella dorsally ornamented with soft bluish-white bristles.

After a while, the spider advanced toward the bush, spreading his forelegs upward. Without stirring an inch from my place, but peeping through the plants, I saw what was happening inside. The female spider, much larger than the male, was resting on a floating Nymphoid leaf. When the male approached her, she raised her forelegs and chased him. The male kept quiet for a few minutes and then again approached her, dancing vigorously and vibrating his legs. If he appeared to be lacking in proper enthusiasm, the female would try to rekindle his interest by vibrating her hind or forelegs. The same procedure was repeated several times. Then, while the female still lay in ambush, the male, all of a sudden, approached her and clutched her tightly.

The preliminary dancing as I later learned sometimes lasts for hours; and the actual mating, in this case, continued for more than fifteen minutes. During this time, I managed to confine the pair, without disturbing them, in a glass tube. When the male released the female, he remained motionless for a moment, then ran toward the end of the tube. Being unable to escape, he came back a few paces. Thereupon the female rushed upon her recent mate, caught him, and stuck her fangs right through the cephalothorax. The poor animal died in a minute or two.

If one were to judge from her appearance and movements, the female was extremely furious. A few minutes later I introduced another male into the tube and the same lot befell him.

I kept the female in captivity, and after sixteen days she laid her eggs and encased them in a pea-like cocoon. It is curi-

ous that this specimen and all the others of various species that
were kept in captivity, invariably laid their eggs at night. The
mother spider under discussion firmly fixed the pea-like
cocoon to her spinnerets and carried it continuously until the
young were hatched, fifteen days later. Immediately upon
emerging from the egg-sac, the young spiders, numbering 167
in all, got upon their mother's back.

Once, I detached the cocoon from the mother's spinnerets
and put it at a distance. But the mother would not be separated from it. She attached it again to her spinnerets as often
as I removed it. I pinned the cocoon to a lump of paraffin. The
mother tried her utmost to snatch it away and, having failed,
attached her spinnerets to it and sat upon it. In this position
no threats would cause her to forsake her instinctive duty of
guarding the egg-sac.

A mother spider cannot distinguish, however, between her
own and another spider's cocoon. When her own cocoon was
exchanged for that of a different species, the spider was quite
satisfied with the substituted one. Several different cocoons,
nearly of equal size, were mixed up. The mother spider was
unable to recognize her own and was satisfied with whichever
one she happened to pick up. It has also been observed that if
an extra cocoon is offered, the spider will sometimes carry it
with the side legs.

These amphibious spiders spend most of their time floating
on water or resting upon leaves or stems of aquatic plants. But
with the approach of evening, they usually retire to land and
seek shelter under cover of near-by vegetation. Sometimes they
climb upon the leaves or stalks of grasses or creep under bricks
and pebbles or into holes in the earth and rest there for the
night. I could find no evidence of any retreat or resting place
made by the spiders themselves either on land or in water.
They are not regular weavers of webs or anything resembling
them, but only spin a little for their cocoons. They are very
quarrelsome. If a male or female happens to be in close proxim-

ity to another male or female a serious quarrel is inevitable. The duel ends in loss of legs, endangering the life of either or both of them.

The female lays eggs in a cocoon of a deep olive color, ornamented with several white spots. The cocoon is composed of two hemispherical cups of silk, joined together with loosely bound white web material, making a line along the equatorial region. With the gradual development of the eggs inside, this white band widens till it gives way for the exit of the young spiders. After coming out of the cocoon the young spiders flock onto their mother's back and remain there for five or six days. These young ones are always in danger of their lives, for neighboring older spiders invariably kill them whenever they catch sight of them.

Though they are of cannibalistic habit, these spiders prey principally upon the water-flies that float upon the surface of the water, the smaller dragonflies, etc. However, they even hunt small fishes whenever there is opportunity.[1] After seizing their prey, they suck the juice out of it by inserting the fangs and crushing the victim with the powerful mandibles.

Sometimes they rest upon the clear surface of water. They cannot walk slowly upon the water surface but cover wide stretches by quick jumps. But their most interesting activities are their maneuvers under water. These spiders, which have been identified as *Lycosa annandalai*, are only one of a number of kinds that have mastered in greater or less degree the aquatic medium and provide a rewarding subject of observation for the naturalist.

[1] The activities of spiders as fishermen have been described by O. Lloyd Meehean in *Natural History*, October, 1934, and by Dr. E. W. Gudger in *Natural History* for January-February, 1931, and in earlier issues.

THE PORTUGUESE MAN-OF-WAR — *A jellyfish of great beauty whose sting can often be fatal* — BY JOSEPH BERNSTEIN.

ONE July day some years ago, two American servicemen stationed in Puerto Rico—a 20-year-old soldier and 27-year-old ensign—went swimming in the ocean. Shortly afterward both of them were carried into the dispensary of the U. S. Naval Hospital.

The appearance of the soldier, according to the attending physicians, "was as though he were recovering from an epileptic convulsion." With eyes staring wildly, and unable to give a coherent account of what had happened, he was propped up on his elbows on the examining table, breathing with such difficulty that each outgoing breath came as a cough. Across his back and left shoulder was an angry, red rash, and the skin of the rest of his body was flushed.

The ensign had a rash on his wrist and abdomen which, he complained, burned severely, and he was perspiring profusely. "There's a load on my chest," he mumbled. "I have to lift my shoulders to breathe." His muscles had contracted to such rock-like rigidity that he could not button his shoes or raise his arms at the shoulder.

Both men had been stung by the jellyfish called the Portuguese man-of-war.

Those who have made voyages far out at sea have often seen numbers of the beautiful blue floats of these jellyfish buoyantly bobbing on top of the roughest waves. At a distance from the shores of Devon and Cornwall, in England, enormous throngs of them have occasionally been seen, forming tremendously long lines and schools. Glowing a brilliant azure blue in bright sunlight, and with crests of a delicate pink hue, they make a strikingly pretty and deceptively innocent sight.

But if you ever come near a Portuguese man-of-war, you had better give it a wide berth and admire it from a generous distance. For contrary to persistent popular belief, it is one of the most dangerous organisms known. Its sting is not only excruciatingly painful but has often been fatal. Native pearl and sponge divers in tropical waters dread it more than the man-eating shark. Only a thick-skinned whale or shark can tangle with the largest of these jellyfish and escape without severe injury.

To the superficial observer, the Portuguese man-of-war looks like a single animal, but in reality it is an amazingly complex colony of great numbers of individuals highly specialized for different functions such as flotation, reproduction, feeding, feeling, and fighting. Colonial jellyfishes of this sort are known as Siphonophores. For all practical purposes, the individual members of this organization are so essential for the preservation of the entire colony that they may be considered as organs of a single body.

The float-organism is a bag often a foot long filled with gas that serves to keep the colony at the surface of the water. By contraction it can expel the gas through a pore and submerge. Later the bag will fill up again through the secretion of gas, thus buoying the colony to the surface. Stretching down from the float, and spreading out in all directions in the water in search of prey, is a mass of threads or tentacles that sometimes reach a length of 50 feet.

Woe betide the hapless creature that gets too near one of these harmless-looking tentacles.

On slightest contact, the batteries of sensitive, triggerlike hairs on these deadly streamers release thousands of small barbs, which sting the animal to death. Slowly the long, snaky tentacles cling tightly around the victim and draw it into con-

tact with the sticky mouths of an array of squirming siphons.
As soon as the fish touches these mouths, which are gluey and
equipped with nettle cells, it sticks fast. The lips of the mouths
are spread out around the fish, so that by the time the victim
is dead, it is inclosed in a tight bag. Here it is digested and
taken into the stomachs of the attached siphons. Nowhere in
the animal kingdom except among the jellyfishes and their
allies is there anything like this amazing trigger-mechanism
for capturing prey.

The barb is really an inverted tube coiled up like a spring
in a box that is covered by a lid. When the trigger-hair on the
box is stimulated by contact and chemical effect, the lid
springs open and the tube shoots out with lightning rapidity,
inverting itself like the finger of a glove. As this happens,
viciously sharp spines on the tube's inner surface unfold to the
outside. These barbs can be used only once. After the threads
are discharged, the jellyfish discards them and grows new ones.

One of the strangest things of all is that a small species of
fish lives in association with the Portuguese man-of-war and is
actually protected by it. These fish swim freely in large numbers among the murderous tentacles, brushing safely against
them without being stung. They amply repay such generous
protection, for their role in this bizarre partnership seems to
be to lure unsuspecting, larger fish within the range of the tentacles.

The Portuguese man-of-war, although widely distributed,
is most frequently found in the open sea in the warmer regions
of the world. It apparently has little control of its own movements and generally drifts about helplessly at the whim of
winds and currents, with the float acting as a sail. It is rather
common from Florida northward, where it is carried by the
Gulf Stream and southerly winds and storms. Frequently it
drifts as far north as the Middle Atlantic and New England
states, where it may be cast up and stranded on the beach.

A warning to bathers who may see these gorgeously hued

jellyfish on the beach: Even after the Portuguese man-of-war has been dead for several days, the tentacles are still capable of inflicting severe stings.

When the creature is out of its tropical environment, its sting seems to be not quite so deadly, though still extremely painful and capable of causing severe illness. Thus Commander A. H. Allen, of the U. S. Naval Medical Corps, reported a case of a woman attacked by three jellyfish which may have been of this kind while swimming in York River, Virginia. She survived but suffered from the effects for several weeks.

Other persons who have been attacked in tropical waters have not been quite so fortunate. A strong, healthy, nineteen-year-old Filipino was working waist-deep in water in a Philippine Island mangrove swamp, gathering firewood. He was clad only in short, cotton drawers. Suddenly he screamed out that something had bitten his leg. One of his fellow workers rushed to him through the 60 yards of water separating them and reached him just as he was about to collapse and in time to prevent his submersion. He was gasping and livid, and was unable to speak, and he was dead by the time he was placed on a raft. Solemnly they brought the dead youth to Dr. H. W. Wade, Chief Pathologist of the near-by Culion Leper Colony of the Philippine Health Service.

"No wound was found," reported Dr. Wade, "except a purplish livid discoloration practically encircling the right leg at the knee." Likewise there was no mark suggestive of snake bite or any other abnormality. None of the boy's companions had seen what had bitten him. Dr. Wade therefore reached the diagnosis that a fairly large, long-tentacled jellyfish had stung him. In all probability the creature was a Portuguese man-of-war. The chief danger to life is not in being stung to death by a jellyfish, according to Dr. Wade, but the possibility of being overcome and drowning before reaching shore.

Still another case of fatal jellyfish stinging was reported

many years ago by Dr. E. H. H. Old in the *Philippine Journal of Science*. Here the victim was a 14-year-old boy, who died "in hysteria" several hours after the sting.

What is the nature of the venomous substance in the stinging cells? Experiments have shown that small animals are promptly killed by eating dried Portuguese man-of-war tentacles. It has been suggested that the poisonous substance is a protein or a mixture of proteins, producing the toxic symptoms through a sharply aggravated allergic reaction. But this theory has been disputed because it would require that the person showing the severe symptoms of an attack be previously sensitized to this type of jellyfish poison. Experience has shown that people who have never seen or been near a jellyfish have frequently suffered severely from the tentacles of a Portuguese man-of-war.

For a long time the standard treatment for jellyfish poisoning was injection of morphine, which generally alleviated the symptoms but was not too successful in effecting speedy recovery. But Dr. M. A. Stuart, of the U. S. Naval Medical Corps, who attended the two servicemen attacked in Puerto Rico, thought that their symptoms looked strangely familiar. Back in the United States he had observed several cases of black widow spider bite. The symptoms were strikingly similar. He had achieved excellent results in treating black widow spider bite with intravenous injections of a solution of calcium gluconate. The standard morphine treatment was tried on the soldier, who felt improvement but did not become entirely well. Dr. Wade decided to try the calcium gluconate treatment on the ensign. The results, according to Dr. Stuart, were "Instantaneous and dramatic." Immediately the patient felt relief from his cramps and oppression in the chest. The local burning was also relieved, and he was now able to lift both arms. He soon was well enough to return to camp.

It is too soon to say that this result means that the venom present in two such dissimilar and unrelated organisms as the black widow spider and the Portuguese man-of-war is basically the same. Further research may eventually supply the answer.

Traditionally we have used the expression "spineless jelly-fish" as a contemptuous epithet for flaccid weakness. But perhaps some day you may be swimming in the ocean, and you may come upon a "spineless jellyfish" under a gay, blue float. Treat it with enormous respect. Better yet, start swimming in the opposite direction.

POOR-ME-ONE *An amazing creature of the tropics whose song is like the wail of a soul in torment* BY WILLIAM E. LUNDY.

MOST persons who love the jungle and turn to it for pleasure and relaxation find an absorbing pastime in listening to the myriad voices that come from its depths. So great is the number and variety of sounds that no single person could name all the creatures heard during a 24-hour period. It may take months or even years to discover the maker of a certain sound, but the thrill of solving such a mystery is ample compensation to the lover of nature.

Should a stranger find himself in our jungles in the Panama Canal Zone, and were he so fortunate as to be able to link all of the calls to their sources, he would find many strange and interesting "ventriloquists." He would hear the roar of lions and the barking of dogs coming from howler monkeys, the laugh of a fat man from a baby alligator, and the whistle of a boy from the snout of a young tapir. He would hear Swainson's Toucan calling with the voice of a frog; and the "dong" of a small silver bell would come from the throat of a tiny tree frog. One of the most deceptive sounds would be the soft bird-like call made by the kitten of the yaguarundi, or "Whistling Cat." No one would imagine that such a sound could come from a feline.

But one voice fascinated me more than any other, and I guess that in all tropical America you could not find an animal that has perplexed and disturbed naturalists the way this one has. It is so utterly unique and weird that it has brought forth comments by many writers over a period of four centuries. It is heard only between dusk and daybreak, and few persons can boast of having spied the creature in the act of making this uncanny call. When the ornithologist Dr. John T. Zimmer heard it in Peru, the natives told him that it was a lost soul— an *alma perdida*—and that he would naturally never be able to shoot it.

Dr. Frank M. Chapman sat spellbound as he listened to this call from the jungle just beyond the clearing of his "Tropical Air Castle" on Barro Colorado Island in the Canal Zone. It had been 37 years since he had heard it before in Trinidad, but he recognized it at once as the call of the "Poor-me-One," a name meaning in the Negro dialect of Trinidad "Poor me, all alone." When describing the experience in 1893, he said, "At first I thought it was a boy. It was a soft but loud, sad, flutelike note. I have never heard such a human sound from a brute before. It made the goose flesh rise all over me." When describing the voice of this creature years later, he said that it had such richness of tone and was so suggestive of sorrow that in all the world of birds or man he had heard none sweeter nor sadder. "So strongly does this song express human emotion," he said, "that one thinks of it as a woman's voice—a deep, mellow contralto calling in hopeless grief."

Gonzalo F. de Oviedo y Valdés, first chronicler of the Indies, is believed to have had this call in mind when four centuries ago he described a sound differing from that of all other animals, beginning with a high note and descending for six points: "Ah, ah, ah, ah, ah, ah."

Doubtless it was the same call that Charles Waterton, an English naturalist and explorer, described in South America in 1816 as being so remarkable that having once heard it, you will never forget it: "When night reigns, . . . you will hear this lamenting like one in distress . . . A stranger . . . would say it was the departing voice of a midnight murder victim, or the wailing of Niobe for her poor children, before she was turned to stone. Suppose yourself in hopeless sorrow, begin with a high note, and pronounce, 'ha, ha, ha, ha, ha, ha, ha' each note lower and lower, till the last is scarcely heard, paus-

ing a moment or two between every note, and you will have
some idea of the moaning."

A few years later an English clergyman, Charles Kingsley,
told of an experience in British Guiana. "Then something . . .
—and I do not deny that it set me more aghast than I had
been for many a day—exploded I say . . . with a shriek . . .
such as I hope never to hear again . . . after which, happily,
the thing, I suppose, went its wicked way, for I heard it no
more . . . for most ghostly and horrible is its cry."

A Balboa resident once told me that she had heard the cry
for the first time when she was alone in her home on Morgan
Avenue and that she thought it was the wife of a neighbor
being beaten unmercifully. She, too, said she hoped never to
hear it again.

All agree that the call of "Poor-me-One," once heard, is not
likely to be forgotten. Residents of Quarry Heights and sections adjacent to Ancon Hill are fortunate—or unfortunate,
according to the point of view—in that they may be awakened
at daybreak by this voice of the jungle. Sometimes it is heard
from nightfall till midnight. On a still night, the cry can be
heard for half a mile; and on moonlight nights, it may come
at intervals throughout the night. I first heard the call from
Ancon Hill in the middle thirties. It so closely fitted the
description given by Dr. Chapman that I knew it must be the
"Poor-me-One." I have heard it many times since.

There has been considerable difference of opinion as to
what creature makes this call. The historian Oviedo gave
credit to the sloth. Probably he was passing along the belief
of the Indians. In any case, this myth has been handed down
for the past four centuries and is still believed by many today.
On the night that Dr. Chapman first heard the call on Barro
Colorado, he called to the keeper, "Donato, what is that calling?" The reply was, *"Perico Ligero,"* a nickname given by the
early Spanish visitors to the Three-toed Sloth. It was the first
time that Dr. Chapman had known Donato to be wrong. A

laborer from southwestern Colombia gave him the same reply, showing how widespread this myth has become.

In 1893, when Dr. Chapman first entered the forests of southern Trinidad, he had been told to listen for the song of the Two-toed Anteater. The notes of the song were described to him so well that when he heard it from the forest he did not doubt its author. After observing a living anteater for some weeks, however, he began to doubt the local belief that it was the "Poor-me-One." A year later he returned to Trinidad and, in company with Albert Carr, a local naturalist who had solved the mystery, actually saw a "Poor-me-One" calling.

What animal, then, had frightened, bewildered, and moved with deep emotion so many jungle travelers?

It was a bird—of the goatsucker group!

If I had had any lingering doubt as to the correctness of this, it would have been wiped out just after daybreak on June 10 of 1950, when I was awakened by an unusually loud cry. From my bedroom window I could see a bird perched on the top of a pole some 40 feet away and silhouetted against the sky. It seemed incredible that this bird, with a length of hardly more than 12 inches, could be the author of a cry of such volume; yet as I watched it, it repeated its loud six-note call. Its body vibrated perceptibly with the force put into each note. Then it flew into the trees across the street, where it called again. The bird returned at dawn on June 12 and again flew away after calling twice. From then until 3:00 A.M. on July 4 it was seen eleven times perching on the pole, preening its feathers, and occasionally darting out a few yards after insects. On two occasions it remained on the pole until it had sung its pathetic song through seven times. After July 4 it was not seen again. Probably the fireworks on that evening had frightened it away to the jungle growth higher on the hill.

Heard from a distance of only 40 feet, the call of "Poor-me-One" has, in addition to the six notes already described by others, a sound like a gasp for breath following each note except the last. One person who had heard it from a short distance thought that the sound was made by flapping the wings against the perch between the notes of the call. I believe it to be made with the throat. In contrast to its famous—or notorious—cry, the bird gave another cry several times. This was low and very deep-throated yet very soft, sounding like "Oo-ah, oo-ah." I doubt that it would be audible at a distance of 100 feet.

Our Panamanian "Poor-me-One" is not consistent in the number of notes used in its song. While the call is usually composed of six notes, the bird has been known to utter eight notes, and several times only four were used. And though I do not yet have visual proof, I am convinced that on rare occasions its cry is reduced to one long heart-rending wail, quite as disturbing in its effects on the listener as is the six-note cry.

Unlike many of its relatives (the nighthawks, whippoorwills, etc.), which perch horizontally on limbs of trees or on the ground, "Poor-me-One" prefers an upright position almost parallel with the perch.

Almost as singular as its calls are the nesting habits of this strange bird. Having selected, through design or instinct, a broken tree stump whose coloring blends well with its own, "Poor-me-One" deposits a single egg in a cavity so placed that it can be incubated while the bird perches in an upright position. Sitting there with its tail pressed firmly against the trunk of the stump, its eyes closed to mere slits, its neck stretched to full length, and its head pointing upward, it becomes to the casual observer a part of the stump itself.

No feathers, twigs, or down line the crude nest, for so well is the cavity selected that little or no room remains for more than the egg. Speaking of a nest that he found in Trinidad, Mr. Alec Muir said, "How the bird managed to place the egg there I cannot imagine. The egg exactly fitted the cavity. There was no room to spare. It could not be moved from side to side, but I could revolve it gently with my fingers."

Within a day or two after hatching, the young bird has assumed the upright posture of its parents, its creamy-white down blending as a patch of fungus on the stump. So tenaciously does it cling to the nest that during its early life it may not be pulled loose without danger of damage to its soft body.

Yes, this is a most extraordinary bird. If you ever hear it call, you will never forget it. Many have fallen under the spell of the jungle—its sights and sounds and smells. But those who have heard it agree that the most haunting song to voice the jungle's timeless mystery and pathos is the call of the "Poor-me-One."

CHRYSANTHEMUM OF THE SEA A
Californian sea worm with flower-like head
BY WOODY WILLIAMS

HAVE you ever reached out for a flower, only to have it van-
ish as if touched by magic? Well, try to take hold of *Eudistylia*.
However, botanists need not search their check lists for this
unfamiliar name, for *Eudistylia* is not a plant.

I found it when wading in the shallow waters of a California bay. The bottom was carpeted with broad fronds of
bright green sea lettuce. Among this growth were gay "chrys-
anthemums"—some orange, some maroon with orange bands.
I knew that many things in the sea are not as they seem. Sea-
weeds twist over the surface to suggest serpents. The coral
gardens of the tropics are not gardens at all but teeming me-
nageries. These creatures, extending from the sandy mud of a
shallow bay, certainly appeared to be escapes from some
autumn garden. But how could they live beneath the sea?

I shuffled toward one and bent down to take it in my hand,
but I came up with only a piece of sea lettuce. I pushed toward
another, the sun behind my back. This time the flower head
vanished before I had come even within reach. These chrysan-
themums in the sea were a lie. Did they exist at all, or was I
a victim of my imagination?

Meanwhile, the tide receded. Among the limp sea lettuce
on the sticky bottom, I saw some tubes projecting above the
surface. A bit of color dripped dejectedly from one tube, but
as I approached, it slid out of sight. This, then, must be my
flower. And I resolved to dig it out with a shovel.

Blisters developed on my hands, and yet the tube went
down and down, curving here and there to circumvent a rock.
The hole I had dug finally extended to arm's length and

beyond. Still the tube descended endlessly. In exhausted desperation, I tugged with all my might. It gave, and I sat down in the mud. In my hand was a parchment-like tube with a broken end. Its full length would have been about three feet. And hanging from it was the broken body of a worm as thick as my forefinger.

The animal slipped out of the tube, and there was my flower! When placed in a jar of sea water, it soon extended again into its former glory. The shape well suggested the local name, "Feather Duster." The worm did not seem greatly to mind the loss of over half of its length, which might have totaled two feet.

This creature was jointed like a "clam worm" or even an earthworm. On the side of each joint were appendages called "parapodia," with which the Feather Duster managed to propel itself up and down in the tube.

Numerous dots covered the tentacles of this gigantic worm, as if pepper had been sprayed over the head. Further examination revealed that these dots were simple eyes—the secret of the Feather Duster's disappearing act. These eyes were the worm's warning system, so that it could flash out of sight at the approach of a mere shadow.

The next time I meet a friend who hasn't seen anything extraordinary for a time, I will take him to a mud flat where *Eudistylia* lives. He will then see some of the strangest sights there are to see, and he will discover that even a worm has learned to lift its head nobly above the muck of a California bay.

THE MOLE'S UNDERWORLD ❧ *He digs day and night in his lightless labyrinths, sometimes even in his sleep* ❧ BY TOM McHUGH.

THE SOD cracked and heaved upward. First one side and then the other of a small ridge were pushed up. Nothing stopped the work of this subterranean earth-cleaver as he forged on through the soil. Stalked plants fell over on their sides and small roots were torn apart with a faint crunching sound.

My curiosity could wait no longer, and I quickly plunged a trowel through the ridge to trap the animal in the blind end of his tunnel. But even that was not enough to corner him. By the time I had brushed away the top of the ridge, the only remaining sign of the creature was a patch of velvety fur and a little pink tail. I rapidly seized the tail and started pulling, but pulling on that organ was about as successful as trying to uproot a small tree—it just didn't work.

Finally, by removing all the earth around him, I succeeded in pulling out all seven inches of a gray furry mass. With his broad, spadelike feet and pointed pink snout, he gave every indication of an animal that was truly "king of the underworld." Few animals have become as specialized for a narrow existence as this common mole.

Putting the mole on a hard-surfaced dirt road was ample proof of this. Completely ill-adapted to walking above ground, he traveled over the road with an awkward waddling gait. The ungainly stride was obviously due to the fact that his legs extended out to the sides, rather than beneath him.

When I placed him on some looser soil, he immediately sought a path of escape. Rather than waddle off into deeper grass, he quickly put his nose to work at finding weak spots in the ground. Placing his forefeet close to his snout, he pushed the earth aside. Again his nose became active, not in boring or in shoving aside the dirt but in discovering a suitable spot to place the feet for the next side stroke.

In less than a few seconds he had completely vanished from the upperworld and its attendant bright colors and pleasant breezes. He had disappeared into a world of damp earthy smells, perpetual darkness, and sounds little stronger than the weak grating noise made by an earthworm inching along through its tunnel. The mole's life is one of blind confinement.

Like most animals that dwell in undying darkness, the mole has very poor eyes. Scarcely the size of a pin head, each one nevertheless contains all the elements of a normal eye. But most of these elements have greatly degenerated, and the mole can probably do no more than tell lightness from darkness.

In the lightless chambers of his underground home, however, the mole needs no vision and no apology. With his naked snout and small pink tail he perceives the earth about him. Both structures are densely covered with sensory cups and tactile hairs. Running from these to the brain, a network of nerve trunks conveys the vital messages. When the mole is backing up in his burrow, the tail serves like an eye in the back of his head. In going forward, the nose is never used for loosening the soil. Rather, it makes rapid and detailed examinations in order properly to direct the powerful claws.

Of course, the mole's ears are also very valuable sense organs. Since big external ears would rapidly become clogged with dirt, the mole has none. Instead, two little skull holes lead into inner organs of hearing that are powerfully developed.

Besides the ears, nose, and tail, other modifications adapt the mole to its subterranean life and complete the story of this remarkable specialization. The fur is velvety and offers scarcely any resistance to the animal's passage within the tunnels. The neck is so short that the forelegs seem to sprout from the sides of the head. With this arrangement, the mole can bring his forefeet together in front of his nose for excavating earth from the end of the burrow.

The big, flipper-like forefeet are the very essence of his moleness. The claws of the forefeet are broad and spadelike, and in digging they are pushed against the earth like so many shovels. Compared with the rapid digging of an animal like the dog, the mole is slow indeed. Unlike the dog, the effectiveness of the mole's claws is not due to the momentum gained before they strike—rather, it is due to the great muscular force with which they are pushed. The large size of the forefeet makes them an adequate base for the enormous claws and gives them a large capacity for transferring piles of loose earth. Even the hind feet are webbed to kick earth through the tunnels.

Although these adaptations have been known for some time, their exact method of use for digging was long a mystery. Since moles do not expose themselves at the surface while burrowing, field studies could give only general ideas concerning the animal's movements.

Naturalists long believed that the mole could easily "swim" through the earth, much in the manner that a person glides through the water by the breast stroke. It took some clever experiments by Dr. F. L. Hisaw to prove that "swimming" was not the usual case.

Dr. Hisaw constructed boxes with glass sides and bottoms so that the burrowing creatures could be watched from the side and from below. In this way he found that progression was, to be sure, made by a swimming motion if the soil was loose. But if the soil was packed until it was as solid as that normally found in nature, the mole did not "swim," but dug.

The digging is done entirely with the forefeet. The way in which these are used can be demonstrated by placing a mole on a table and holding it down with the palm of the hand. The mole might be expected to resist this force by raising its body and struggling out, but it does not. Instead, it rotates its body, puts one forefoot on the table and the other against the hand, and pushes with a slow but strong motion.

Moles use the same type of movement when they are excavating their surface runways. One foot is placed on the floor of the tunnel while the other pushes the earth up to form a ridge. The sod is thrown up on the right and then on the left and in front. There is every appearance of industrious work as the mole presses forward at the rate of about 12 to 15 feet an hour.

Besides these surface runways, which are used for collecting food, moles also dig deep passages, which are used as headquarters and for thoroughfares to feeding grounds. The deep tunnels may be from six inches to two feet below the surface of the soil.

At this depth the earth cannot be pushed upward or to the side. Instead, it must be loosened and carried away. After a quantity of dirt is freed and piled in the tunnel behind the mole, the animal turns about and pushes the earth out of the burrow with one of its broad paws.

As the soil is forced up through the entrance, it falls down on all sides and forms the familiar mounds that we call "mole hills." Sometimes this earth may be packed into a discarded part of the tunnel system.

Like most people, moles eventually become discontented with their homes and begin remodeling. Whereas human beings rebuild their houses for better appearance, the mole does so for food. As the mole remodels, he drives a new tunnel beneath the old, pushing the earth into the discarded burrow above.

This seems to be a clever way of saving labor. The remodeling is obviously for the purpose of feeding on earthworms and insect larvae, which require moist earth. If the animal were to construct an entirely new system deep enough to reach this food, he would not only have to break the hard dry surface but would also have to remove much earth to reach the proper depth.

Since these tunnels are a vital defense against predators from the outer world, breaks in them are rapidly repaired. Soon after a rupture occurs, a little pink snout appears and cautiously explores the opening. The snout is quickly withdrawn, and, within a minute, the break is plugged with a mass of soil.

Moles even use their digging habits to capture dangerous prey. They have been known to force earth against the nests of yellow-jackets until the insects were completely crushed or smothered. The attacking mole then safely devoured both the young and adults.

The mole's adaptations have confined him to a life in lightless labyrinths. The round of his experiences consists mainly of smells of fresh moist earth, plant roots, and various worms and grubs he seeks out for food. Digging hangs so heavily on his mind that he may sometimes be seen going through the motions of digging even in his sleep.

These earth-cleaving and feeding habits do not go completely unobserved, especially if they appear in the garden or on the golf course. Prized daffodils are felled, and key golf shots are shaken from their course.

Fortunately, there are two sides to the matter. Moles are injurious only when they appear in concentrated gardens or in golf courses. Elsewhere they do a world of good by eating large numbers of destructive insects. In fact, just one mole can consume about 40,000 insects and worms each year.

Through the ages they have also played an important part in the evolution of the soil. By constantly moving and stirring it, bringing up subsoil, and carrying down organic matter from the surface, they have contributed to the natural building up of soil fertility.

With man's occupancy of the land, the value of moles as cultivators ceases. Their natural process is much too slow. But in the uncultivated areas of the earth, the little king of the underworld still remains a useful citizen—the symbol of one of Nature's most complete and successful ventures into the realm of subterranean darkness.

❧ COCOON, FAMILY SIZE ❧ *The African processionary caterpillars spin one giant envelope in which to pupate* ❧ BY JAMES P. CHAPIN, ASSOCIATE CURATOR EMERITUS OF BIRDS, THE AMERICAN MUSEUM OF NATURAL HISTORY.

THIS silken pouch may have contained 300 or 400 individual cocoons, for it was spun by a great number of African "processionary" caterpillars, so sociable that they enclose themselves in one large envelope when about to pupate.

The largest of such "nests" may weigh as much as a pound, and for many years efforts have been directed toward the utilization of this "wild silk." Strong, but not lustrous, the threads can be utilized for some fabrics, for sewing-silk, and for the insulation of cables. But since this silk has been spun by a number of individual caterpillars, it is not possible to reel it from the cocoon, and the thread differs from that of true silkworms by having "knots" at rather regular intervals.

During World War II, when there was such a vital need for rubber, quinine, minerals, and other materials that could be produced in Africa, attention was given in West Africa to the gathering of this wild silk. It was said to be needed in England for the making of parachutes.

The nest shown elsewhere in this book was brought in 1942 to the Forestry Officer, Mr. W. B. Collins, at Juaso in the Ashanti Forest of the Gold Coast. The caterpillars that made it were probably the young of the moth named *Anaphe venata*, this being the only form of *Anaphe* reported from the Gold Coast as late as 1930, though there are four other related species, widely distributed in tropical Africa and Madagascar. The adult moths are dull and whitish, with a few brown or blackish bars on the wings. The wingspread is a little more than a couple of inches.

It is not likely that *Anaphe* nests will retain any great commercial value in times of peace, for cultivation of the domestic silkworm has been undertaken with great success in recen' years in the northeastern corner of the Belgian Congo.

🞐 THE DUSKY GLIDER 🞐 *A flying possum from Australia that gallops up tree trunks and soars over 250 feet* 🞐 BY DAVID FLEAY.

ONE of the really remarkable mammals in Australia is the largest species of parachuting or gliding possum—the Dusky Possum Glider or Greater Glider (*Schoinobates volans*). In over-all length, this skinny-framed "flying rope walker" may total 40 inches, but over half of this is taken up by the pendulous, bushy tail. And though appearing to be a big creature, its weight averages a mere three pounds.

Normally dusky-black in color, with long, soft, and silky fur, the somber-hued creature is highly specialized for life among the great eucalypts of the eastern and southeastern highlands of Australia. The animal ascends the trunks of the gums with an extraordinary galloping motion, and when it lands at the end of an 80- to 90-yard swoop, its extremely sharp claws readily grasp the hard, smooth trunk of the tree.

Fully as distinctive as the Dusky Glider's unusual appearance is its musky, eucalyptus oil odor; and though the animal is thoroughly dainty and clean in a "gummy" fashion, it is not long before the lofty hollows that form its daylight retreats acquire this pungent though by no means disagreeable odor of musk and bruised gum leaves.

Although the Dusky Glider is the most numerous of the larger arboreal furred creatures in the forested mountain country of eastern Australia, it is one of the most delicate and difficult marsupials to maintain in captivity. It is the only gliding possum that is a leaf eater, and unless it is able to secure a select variety of eucalypt foliage, it simply will not live. In this respect it resembles the koala. Its diet is close to that of the common Ring-tailed Possum (*Pseudocheirus*), which most

58

nearly represents the ancestral stock of the Dusky Glider. In both, the skull characters, teeth, and facial appearance are similar. In fact, we might call the Dusky Glider the "Flying Ringtail" of the really big timber. The true Ringtail lives in the lower levels and cannot find a toe hold on the almost glass-smooth trunks of the great trees.

In typical specimens, there is a white area underneath, contrasting with the black of the back and tail. The large ears are thickly covered with fur on the outside but not on the inside. These, coupled with the bare pink nose and solemn eyes, invest the animal with that somber and wistful expression so often observed when it gazes forth from a lofty hollow after someone has tapped the base of the tree with an ax. Though normally dusky-black, the general color is variable, ranging from dark animals, through others with smoke-gray flanks, to almost white and really white animals.

One of these large gliders shooting down through space on its aerial jaunts looks for all the world like a swiftly diving kite. Its volplaning membrane, unlike that in the genus *Petaurus* (Sugar and Yellow-bellied species), does not extend from the outer digit of the "hand" to the ankle of the hind foot. It stretches from the elbow of each forelimb to the ankle. Therefore, while in midair with the membrane outstretched, the animal tends to assume more of a triangular shape, with the apex forward.

The home tree of the Dusky Glider is usually a large gnarled and knotted old giant, as often dead as not, and the nesting hole is high up in the trunk. From these daylight havens the inhabitants may be seen coming forth at deep dusk, stopping to comb their fur and scan the world of big trees before going about their nightly business. Nests of stripped bark or leaves are built in these retreats, but it appears that the black gliders are casual about embellishing their comforts. The species has apparently lost a good deal of the collecting and architectural ability of its Ringtail forebears.

The home trees are usually betrayed by varying degrees of shredding or scratching of the bark (depending on whether it is the stringy or smooth type), where the well-developed claws have scored the surface in "landing." To the experienced eye, the characteristic cross scratches on hard-barked eucalypts tell of frequent skidding stops made by volplaning possums.

One is usually able to determine whether the inhabitants are at home by striking resounding blows on the trunk with an ax. Soon a shaggy head may gaze forth, followed by the total emergence of one or two animals. Finding the vibration unpleasant, they proceed to climb upward with their characteristic galloping motion until finally they perch on the topmost point of the tree, their long tails waving loosely in the wind. Further blows at this juncture usually cause the animals to bunch up and leap forth, and then to glide away down some well-known aerial track to the safety of a trunk 40, 60, or even 80 yards away.

The mention of aerial tracks is not an exaggeration. Time and again I have noticed that, in springing forth with outstretched limbs from the upper boughs of their home trees, and setting out for nocturnal feeding grounds, Dusky Gliders travel in stages, using the same trees for landing and lobbing each time at much the same spot on the lower trunk.

Usually when tapped gently forth from an upper hollow, gliders wait until quiet reigns once more and then return slowly to the hole, rolling the long tail into a furry ring at the moment of re-entry. This action leads me to believe that when transporting nesting material, this animal may quite possibly carry it in a twist of the tail, just as I have seen the Ring-tailed Possum and the Sugar Glider do.

The momentum that carries the glider such great distances is gained from the initial, almost vertical dive. Naturally, the higher the starting point, the farther the creature is able to glide. After the dive, it flattens out and finally sweeps gently upward for a landing, thus reducing the shock of its impact with the tree. Having lobbed, the glider climbs with its curious gallop into higher regions.

The Greater Glider, so much at home in the treetops and in the air, is a ludicrous sight on open ground. Its progress is extremely awkward and slow and may best be described as an undulating gallop—the main object being to find something to climb and find it quickly. Occasionally, however, either by accident or design, the animals do appear to journey across open spaces, risking destruction by the fox.

By observing captive specimens, I found that these strict leaf eaters were extremely fond of the common peppermint (*Eucalyptus australiana*) and Long-leaved Box (*E. elaeophora*). To a lesser extent they took Swamp Gum (*E. ovata*), Manna Gum (*E. viminalis*), Apple Box (*E. stuartiana*), Mountain Gray Gum (*E. goniocalyx*), River Red Gum (*E. camaldulensis*), and several species of stringy bark, but they showed a definite dislike for many other species. The almost cosmopolitan taste of other herbivorous possums, such as the Silver Gray and Ringtail, for succulent young leaves of almost any description is certainly not shared by *Schoinobates*.

Animals kept in confinement may be persuaded to acquire an additional taste for bread and milk spread with sweet jam or honey, but this is only possible as an adjunct to the diet of eucalypt leaves. Melon and lemon jam is a favorite with the Dusky Glider, just as it is with numerous other marsupials.

It is interesting to note that, apart from the consideration of diet, the animals will not thrive in captivity unless supplied with a log or box fitted after the style of a "home tree" and situated in a lofty position in a roomy enclosure. Long sapling poles and stringy bark boughs are also provided, for seldom, unless sick, will the Dusky Glider descend to the floor of its cage.

The breeding habits of the Dusky Glider are similar to those of other members of the possum family, except that the development of the offspring is rather slow. Like other possums, it is a pouched animal, or marsupial. Only two mammae are found in the pouch, and as in the genus *Trichosurus* (the Silver-gray and Short-eared Possums), only one embryo is reared at a time. In Victoria, this minute naked creature seems to appear usually in July or August; and it is difficult to realize that such a mite, no longer than the head of a thumbtack, may indulge some day in graceful aerial "flights."

Like any other young marsupial, it makes its early journey into the pouch entirely under its own steam. Gradually as the youngster increases in bulk, it becomes evident that the limbs and tail are extraordinarily long, and the loose volplaning membrane from fore to hind legs is plainly visible. The color of the furless embryo is pink, with very dark ears. Naturally, all inspections of the pouch are conducted under difficulties, for the mother resents the handling, and there is also considerable danger of harming the infant.

The joey (as we call the young) appears to become free of its attachment to the mother when some six weeks of age. It is then able to attach itself to the source of nourishment or relinquish it at will. Later the eyes open, and a covering of short fur indicates more plainly than in the adult the contrast between the black and white upper and lower surfaces.

Between the time of growing fur and the forsaking of the mother's "pocket nursery," the young Dusky Glider is one of the most curious and pathetic babes that one can imagine. Lanky legs, very long tail, and thin, weedy body combine to produce a most extraordinary little creature. There is a period during which the little joey spends its daylight hours outside the maternal shelter and is carried about in it by night. Before the animal is four months old it has outgrown the pouch (though it still gets its nourishment there), and then the little glider may cling to its mother's back during her nocturnal wanderings. Her gliding leaps are then no longer possible unless the youngster remains in the home tree or sleeping hollow.

Throughout 1925-27, I had in captivity a pair of Dusky Gliders from the Daylesford district, and during this time they produced several young. Generally the single joey arrived in early August, but strange to say, none of these offspring grew to maturity; they died shortly after leaving the pouch. Later, in more successful experiments I found that particular care was necessary as the weaning phase was reached. The baby animal required a most careful selection of gum tips, not only in regard to species but also to the maturity and delicacy of the branch tips themselves.

You may wander under the trees without ever discovering the Dusky Gliders feeding overhead, unless you listen intently. Perhaps the faint sound of a leaf being pulled from a stalk, or a sudden rustle as the animal shifts its weight from one slender limb to another, betrays its position to a searching torch beam held so that the observer's eyes look straight along the path of light. Then the blazing orbs of the animal, certainly the most brilliant light reflectors I know of among marsupials, regard the intruder with curiosity. But this curiosity is scarcely sufficient to interrupt the meal. Soon the glider puts forth a long forearm to pull more leaves within reach or moves to a more favorable position, its rangy shape and very long tail dimly silhouetted against the starry heavens.

The startling and extraordinary call of the Dusky Glider, heard so frequently in the tall bush by night, particularly in the late autumn, is one of the animal's most distinctive characteristics. It is a loud gurgling shriek running down the scale in a bubbling or even chuckling fashion, accelerating though diminishing in volume. It is uttered mainly while the marsupials are moving actively and indulging in gliding leaps. One hears the initial loud notes, then a rapid gurgle diminishing perhaps with the increase in distance, for by then the swiftly traveling vocalist is shooting at speed to a point perhaps 80 yards farther on through the trees. The calling ceases upon its arrival, when the characteristic "clop" of landing is heard.

From close watching and listening, I think it is certain that these cries are a means of keeping in touch, because members of a pair move through the bush on a "follow the leader" principle. The animals are particularly attached to each other, and the gurgling shrieks, so typical of the deep forest, are really signal cries—an accomplishment far beyond the powers of non-gliding possums and one that was probably developed in conjunction with their powers of flight.

It is fortunate that from a commercial point of view the Dusky's skin is extremely thin and papery and that the soft silky fur lacks permanent rigidity. This, combined with the fact that the animals have an inseparable attachment for dense forest lands and do no economic damage whatever, makes it unlikely that man will molest them. Bush fires, however, are the scourge and bane of these animals. They become utterly helpless, and I have watched them twirling in agonized bewilderment down into the onrush of consuming flames. In the holocaust of early 1939, tens of thousands of these volplaning creatures perished in the Victorian ranges, and many that survived in odd sheltered gullies died subsequently of starvation, because the leaves of their food trees were either consumed by fire or were blasted and withered. For weeks after the flames had died on Mount Riddell and Mount Toolebewong, we found tortured Dusky Gliders crawling weakly over the charred ground, their black color camouflaging them amid that desolate world of stark, dreary ashes.

The extraordinary rehabilitation of the species after the dreadful fire is remarkable, considering that a pair of Dusky Gliders rears but a single youngster a year. In the middle 1940's, during many nocturnal quests on the slopes of Mount Riddell, Healesville, I was amazed to find the big gliders quite numerous again. Certainly the deep valley of Badger Creek was not entirely devastated by fire, but judging from the surviving stock in this valley, and perhaps in others far away, it is evident that an increase must have occurred.

The Dusky's one consistent enemy is the Powerful Owl, a great bird of the night that is really dependent on the Dusky Glider and Ring-tailed Possum for its meals. This largest yet shyest of Australian owls dwells in the same country as the Dusky. While I was making a special study of this little-known bird of prey, I was amazed to find that it carried off at least one Dusky Glider or Ringtail practically every night. In denser ranges, the victims were usually Dusky Gliders. It is indeed fortunate that the Powerful Owl is a rare bird and therefore makes little impression on the population of this plentiful animal.

FISHING FOR BATS ❧ BY C. R. PARTIK.

I AM a native of Quebec Province and lived for 20 years in the country north of the St. Lawrence River, where the winters are really old-fashioned. Recently I moved 50 miles south to be a little nearer civilization.

On August 29, 1944, after work, I rowed out on Lac Long, near Ste. Agathe Des Monts, Quebec, to cast a festive fly to the big trout that had begun to come in to inspect their spawning grounds and were rising to nothing in particular.

Among my Numbers 10 to 16 there was nothing that roused their interest, and I knew that further effort would be wasted. It was one of those rare early autumn evenings for which the Laurentian hills are famous, and I let the breeze take my boat where it might. The sun had disappeared over the purple hills and the shadows had crept across the lake when the boat halted near the mouth of the creek.

Presently in the waning light I noticed what looked like a small minnow wriggling to the surface; it was the last stage in the metamorphosis of the May fly (Plectoptera). The little creature's back split open immediately and from it emerged the now complete insect, ready to take to the air within a few seconds when its wings were fully straight.

Then from nowhere in the semi-darkness appeared a bat. Without hesitation it dove to the surface of the water, cleverly picked up the newborn insect, and disappeared.

I happened to have in my fly box an excellent imitation of the May fly on a No. 10 hook. (This fly is known to fly fishing enthusiasts as Green Drake.) I put it on my leader, gave it a good coat of fat to make it float, and cast it about 20 feet from the boat.

Hardly had my artificial creation dropped on the water,

and before I could twist my wrist enough to pull the fly under, the bat reappeared, picked it up, and was hooked. It made one or two attempts to get up into the air, but without success.

Slowly I retrieved my line to release the bat, being careful not to set the hook more than necessary; but by one last effort the creature freed itself and flew away.

I made several more casts in various directions. Every time the fly landed on the water, this or another bat was back. Only by close attention and immediate action could I prevent the creature from getting hooked. And I was reminded that, at least in this light, it would be wrong to say "as blind as a bat."

❧ THE MOST AMAZING TONGUE IN NATURE
❧ *The chameleon's rapid-fire tongue is longer than its body* ❧ BY ROBERT CUSHMAN MURPHY, CHAIRMAN, DEPARTMENT OF BIRDS, AMERICAN MUSEUM OF NATURAL HISTORY.

AT FIRST you see nothing but a tangle of green, nearly leafless vine, supported by a few dead black twigs. Next, the tiny flashing of opalescent wings shows that a host of insects is scattered throughout the labyrinth. They seem to be the only denizens of this microcosmic African jungle.

But look sharply, for something is happening to one of the sticks; it is conjuring itself into a black, lifeless-looking creature with withered limbs. It might have died a month or a year ago, only to dry up on the stalks it resembles.

Look beyond, among yellowish-green withes of the vine, and you will spy a similarly ancient object, except that this one is of an olive tone like the surroundings in which it lodges.

But the black monster in front is coming to life. It has shifted its skinny hands, with barely perceptible movements, to a neighboring twig, and now, with the stealthiness of only a chameleon, it pulls its length along after them. Sneakingly, ever so softly, the crooked hind feet loose their hold upon the first perch. The tail, likewise looped around it, sluggishly uncoils; all but motionless actions gradually transfer the spellbound lizard to its chosen point of vantage. Then, splitting its cloven feet around the new twig, it awaits the gifts of fortune.

Stillness is its first principle, and yet its frozen pose is not quite complete, for uncanny eyes that work like independent searchlights continually jerk about without any sign of a common purpose. The eyes are housed in cone-shaped barrels, and

68

by using each singly the chameleon can look in any direction without a bend of the spine or a crook of the neck. While one impossible eye is star-gazing, the other is directed backward. Suddenly the creature stares straight ahead in a moment of bifocal vision, but just as abruptly one tube of the disjointed optics pops out at a right angle to the head, and the small bright orb—the sole convincing sign of inner life—bears upon an oblivious fly a foot away. Not a stir anywhere escapes the intent reptile, whereas its own movements are now limited to the manipulation of its telescopes.

The chameleon, as an embodiment of patience, is the Job of Nature. He wastes no time in pursuing nimble insects. You might surmise that he understands the law of chance. A fly walks up his shrunken, weather-beaten, leather side and receives no more attention than the proverbial gnat on a bull's horn. A fly settles on the twig behind him, but his only response is to point briefly one sleepless evil eye; the other is likely to be functioning simultaneously elsewhere. What kind of image can such dissociated equipment produce in the little ogre's none too excellent brain?

At last a blissful fly has alighted upon a twig nine or ten inches from the chameleon's snout. In the first response of concentrated attention, the watcher's cannon-like eyes swing forward in their shriveled portholes and hold a common aim. The fly, with naught in its world to disturb it, ceases to stroke its wings. The whole scene is one of rest. The chameleon opens his hard, dinosaurian jaws slightly, as if to yawn, and from the mouth a clubby pink tongue protrudes. An inch, two inches, three inches it slides slowly forth. How futile! A good seven-inch span of safety lies between the slimy tip of the tongue and its intended victim.

Perhaps the chameleon has given up hope, for, quicker than human sight can follow, the tongue snaps back into the mouth. But wait—the insect has not flown. It has merely vanished, and to the hunter we must turn for an explanation, be-

cause the hunted has had no time to know that anything has
happened! From its comfortable isolation to the grinding mill
of the jaws it has been whisked in a twinkling. The mouth of
the living corpse is champing, though silently, and the burning
eyes are once more peering askew toward unsuspecting flies
among the vines.

For more than a century the mechanism of this accomplished tongue has presented a fascinating problem to naturalists. It has long been known that a chameleon with a
seven-inch body can shoot a fly twelve inches from its nose,
and that the whole process is comparable in speed with a flash
of lightning. The way in which the tongue is used, therefore,
offers a unique opportunity for studying nervous and muscular
organization, and the details have been learned only within
the last few years.

The plan of the weapon might be said to combine certain
features of the stretched rubber bands of a slingshot with the
extraordinary propelling force obtained by squeezing a wet
watermelon seed from the tips of thumb and forefinger.

The tongue, together with the hyoid bones that form its
basal support, represents only a modification of the familiar
equipment of all backboned animals. It consists of a fleshy
terminal knob armed with "mucilage," and an extensible hollow stalk. Into the soft, partly inverted tube of the stalk the
knob fits when it is retracted. The bones and their muscles are
so arranged that the root of the tongue can be carried forward
remarkably close to the tip of the lower jaw. In the mouth the
tongue remains always in a position of readiness. In other
words, the spring is set before the chameleon pulls the trigger.

The massive tongue knob is a ring-muscle, known to anatomists by the expressive term *musculus accelerator linguae*. It
is made up of a series of circular discs around a sheath, and
each disc is composed in turn of small bundles of radiating
fibers, the directions of which are reversed in alternate discs.
It is the sharp contraction of the ring-muscle on the tapering

and slippery end of the median hyoid bone that causes the astounding explosion a second or two after the end of the tongue has been slowly thrust from the mouth, pulled by hyoid muscles on either side and drawing the expanding stalk behind it.

The projectile, however, must not only strike its game but must also bring it back. This is the point at which the elastic stalk serves the function of a lanyard. When at rest, the tube of the stalk is shortened and thickened along its bony peg, the forward end enclosing the base of the knob like a turned-back glove finger. Within its walls the muscle-strands, nerves, and blood vessels are thrown into folds more intricate than the twists of any meandering river. Not the least surprising part of the whole rapid insect-catching proceeding is that such delicate tubes and tracts can be jerked out to the taut limit of their extension without rupturing.

The routine, when the chameleon brings his artillery into play, is, therefore, somewhat as follows: first, the stimulus of the prey, which comes to the lizard only by sight; second, the complicated nervous response that causes it to open its mouth and slowly stick out the tongue knob while at the same time it is calculating aim and range with its two converging eyes; third, the fly-catching snap which comes when protrusion is succeeded by projection; and fourth, the final process of retraction or snapback, which carries the prey into the mouth, thus starting mastication and releasing the eyes for divided attention to the world roundabout.[1]

Fossil bones of the chameleon's probable ancestors have only recently been discovered in Cretaceous rock, laid down toward the end of the Age of Reptiles, perhaps 70 million years' ago. The various kinds of chameleons that live in the world of today, however, must be regarded as modern and very highly

[1] The structure and physiology of the chameleon's tongue, as studied since the year 1805, are covered in the text and bibliography of a paper by Dr. C. P. Gnanamuthu, in the *Proceedings of the Zoological Society of London, 1937*, Vol. 107, pp. 1-63.

specialized lizards despite their primordial aspect that suggests the boredom of remembered eons. As is evident, their talents are few but adequate—otherwise the weird little beasts would not have survived for parvenu man to watch. Their power to change color, which enhances the concealing effect of motionlessness, has become a metaphor. The tongue, which goes forth on such long forays to bring home the bacon in small but frequent portions, would be sufficiently astonishing in a fever-heated creature like a humming-bird. As the food-gatherer of a being characterized by cool blood and profound torpor, it must be classed as one of the foremost marvels of evolution.

❦ THE MOST FASCINATING PERFUME ON EARTH ❦ *The tiny musk deer's sachet lures hunters to the roof of the world* ❦ BY JENNIE E. HARRIS.

How DID a tiny deer in the highlands of central and eastern Asia ever become connected with the perfume on my dressing table?

The answer lies so far back in antiquity that it's lost—perhaps as far back as the beginning of Chinese history.

Here is a shy, sensitive creature, about the size of a half-grown Bambi, scarcely 20 inches tall at his shoulders, wandering among rhododendrons at an altitude of 8000 feet and higher. The little animal has no antlers. Two curving teeth project from his upper jaw like ivory daggers. His body springs amazingly fast; his hind quarters are always elevated for easy leaping. And near the base of his abdomen is that walnut-sized pouch that puts his life in constant peril.

This pouch holds a quantity of musk-grains tiny as millet seed when dried, as large as peas when moist. When he rests on a rock, the musk is exposed; and when he darts away, the sun, heating the rock, diffuses the scent, giving evidence of his recent presence. The perfume is strongest when the musk is a fresh, oily, gingerbread-like substance, and one tiny grain of it can perfume millions of cubic feet of air.

He leaps high among the junipers, rhododendrons, and birches, nibbles at moss and lichen, and sags upon the forest floor, his coarse, grayish-brown hair blending with the leaf-shadows which render him obscure. But his dark eyes are wary, for he must hiss and be off on all fours at the first strange sound or smell.

Musk hunters trail him with dogs and guns. They observe where he feeds, noting how gentians and primroses are

73

thinned out a little and how a stringy, white lichen that festoons trees shows signs of his nibbling. They set snares and traps where he might return to dine. Or they hurl arrows tipped with aconite to stop his sure-footed bounding.

To trap numerous deer, hunters build a palisade of prickly bushes in a suitable defile. Then they spread out fanwise in all directions and rush back screaming and waving their arms—frightening the timid deer in an ever-narrowing arc, on and on into the trap of greenery.

The high-up deer remains cautious. Perhaps he manages to elude dogs, guns, snares, traps—even the deceiving palisade. He stays deep among the thickets, eating lichen or the musk-tasting sumbul roots. But what's this sudden, weird, sweet music? It is like bird music, but music from a bird he has never heard before. It draws him from his hiding, and when he is out in the open, seeking the source of that wild music, the hunter lays down his flute. The little deer's love of music has been his final betrayal.

Sportsmen seldom aim at a musk deer, though his venison is a great delicacy and his coarse, brittle, hollow hair makes resilient mattresses for Tibetan travel. But commercial musk-hunters think little of sportsmanship. They want his musk—that most powerful, penetrating, and enduring odor known. They want the money musk is worth—$560 a pound as it reaches the market, according to a recent Du Pont Company report; $40,000 a pound if it could reach its final destination in a pure form.

The musk is often adulterated. The hunter leans over the dead deer and cuts away the little pouch with its covering of hide and hair. Then, instead of continuing down the trail, he rushes the pouch to a near-by hut while it is still soft, still newly taken. He pokes and stretches its natural opening so as to be able to remove the grains with as little loss as possible. The minute the fresh musk is exposed to the air, it expands and effervesces. If he tried to poke the true musk back into the pouch, the pouch might not hold it all. Besides, he is not ready yet. First, he mashes up acorns, fried liver, dried peas, dried grain, or dried blood with the moist, oily musk, making a curious dark mass. He stuffs part of this mixture among the membranes in the pouch, and the rest he puts into another pouch of hide and hair which he has faked.

Then he rubs his smelly hands in satisfaction. He knows that the mashed acorn, liver, peas, and blood will take on the peculiar, powerful scent of the musk and will themselves impart that scent to whatever they touch.

After this hasty preparation, he takes the trail; but the smell of the perfume is on him, and the knowledge that he has extracted musk is on other men's minds. All along the downward trail, the brown nut passes from man to man, from murderer's hand to murderer's hand.

The caravan that transports the musk radiates the musk-scent, announcing the journey as clearly as would a streaming light or a ringing bell. Bandits swoop down upon it like vultures; whole caravans have been wiped out and merchant trains wrecked for a few pouches of musk.

Musk has been taking a toll of 100,000 deer a year—females as well as males, although the former do not have the musk pouch. Except for his two canine teeth that give the appearance of tusks, the buck resembles the doe, and those two teeth are not easily descried at rifle distance.

Although the musk develops in the male only after he is two years old, hunters capture young deer, too. The white-spotted little creatures are born one or two at a time and go bounding off on their solitary way within six weeks. Even if the animal is snared rather than shot, so delicate a creature can easily be injured before it is freed.

Does the deer smell the musk upon himself—that perfume stronger than he is, from which he can never quite escape? The odor is part of his mating lure and is most pungent in spring, when the pouch holds a soft, unctuous, light-tinted mass. Later, it becomes darker and grainy.

Musk is said to be the most fascinating of all scents to man. Mohammed wrote in the Koran, about 600 A.D.: "The Seal of Musk. For this let those pant who pant for bliss." Empress Josephine, Napoleon's wife, used musk as her personal perfume. Years afterward, the walls of her apartments still gave aromatic proof of this. Even with extreme adulteration, its odor is highly, magnetically sweet.

Chinese buyers, suspecting adulteration, are reported to enlarge the natural opening in a pod with a thick, blunt needle. With a hooked, silver needle, they probe about inside for any foreign substance the needle might touch. They extract a tiny sample, examine its color. Pure musk is yellow, yellow-red, reddish-brown, or purple. They smell it. The scent of pure musk is luxurious, rich, and full. They rub a tiny bit between a moistened thumb and forefinger. Pure musk won't form a paste, but stays intact. They test the pod for its pliability; if all is unmolested inside, the pod responds to touch, shrinks away, and seems to quiver a little. In addition, there are tests of fire, caustic potash and soda, and ammonia solution.

Musk is sold in "pod" or "grain." According to encyclopedias, grain musk means the substance removed from the pod, and it includes hair. The pods are packed, 20 or 30 in a cannister lined with tin, and covered with silk of a peculiar Chinese design. Tonquin Musk from Tibet is usually highest in esteem; Cabardine Musk from China or Russia is next in importance.

The dried pods give off little odor, but pods soaked back to natural plumpness exhale their intense, penetrating scent. Musk must throw off particles of itself to be smelled at all. Yet scientific experiment proves that a few grains of musk will perfume a large hall for years without appreciable loss of weight.

The muskrat trapped in our United States marshes has

musk; and musk odor is strong in the Australian musk-duck and other animals. The Ross Allen Institute at Silver Springs, Florida, has received requests for musk extracted from alligators and has supplied samples. Yet, no musk has qualities for perfumery comparable to that of the little musk deer.

The musk deer lives in a setting of bewildering beauty. At altitudes of 8000 feet and higher in the Himalayas northwest of Szechwan grow forests of rhododendrons found nowhere else in the world. There are parasitic rhododendrons with snow-white bells seven inches long; great tree rhododendrons 30 feet tall, with creamy-tinted flowers and pale pink bark that peels off in flakes, leaving a stem smoothly gleaming like silk; rhododendrons with flowers of vermilion, scarlet, crimson, rose, purple, yellow, or white, strewing the ground with color; and dwarf rhododendrons. Ferns and fernlike bamboos climb the slopes, and there are bronze and green junipers. Perhaps in the far background, Kanchen-junga or the Everest group soars majestically into the glacial blue of the sky.

Such are the scenes that form the homeland of the musk deer, across the highlands of central and eastern Asia and into southern Siberia. Apparently, he has a highly refined appetite for certain flowers, roots, leaves, and lichens. He possesses, it would seem, in his little aesthetic soul, a love for flute music, and in his pouch he carries the most powerful, most exalting "fixative" known.

Perfume makers tell us that a perfume never contains a single odor. It would not be perfume if it did; it would be blatant, brassy, harsh. It must be softened, toned down by other odorous notes and mellowed, so that the result is a subtlety of fragrance.

All perfumes contain selections from odor-types called "sweet," "acid," "burnt," "goat,"—which means that often the vilest odors enter the most enchanting perfumes. Yet, these are utilized in such a way that their own unpleasantness is canceled out, and they enhance the desirable effects of other odors. Moreover, most fragrances have short lives, and there is a belief that musk adds permanence to other odors with which it is mixed. There is some debate as to whether any of the so-called "fixatives" actually do this, but the word has become well established and can hardly be avoided.

There are three other animal products comparable to musk: civet, castor, and ambergris. Ambergris is produced by the sperm whale. It apparently results from some illness, and it is either ejected by the whale to float ashore or is found inside a harpooned animal. It seems to have something to do with the whale's diet of squids and may be comparable in some ways to a gall stone. Most pieces of ambergris weigh only a few ounces or pounds, but lumps weighing 100 pounds or more are sometimes found. One piece, found by a London merchant in 1898, weighed 270 pounds and sold for about $80,000. Fatty and clammy-looking, ambergris cannot be adulterated without easy detection. Its odor is said to be earthy, and it helps to mellow other odors in perfume. It is usually yellow, gray, or black on the outside, with gold, yellowish red, or other colored specks showing through the cracks.

Castor comes from the Canadian and Russian beaver. Canadians trap beavers mostly for their fur, so that castor in Canada is largely a by-product. Both male and female beavers have castor. It is yellow when fresh and later turns reddish brown. The smell is balsamy and the taste bitter. It imparts an "oriental note" to perfume and helps in blending.

Civet smells horrible. Yet, it must be rather pleasant in extreme dilution if early Italians and Spaniards used it, as we are told, to perfume gloves. It comes from the male and female civet cat of Abyssinia and India. The cats are teased while enclosed in a cage too small for them to fight back. This angers them to the extent that they pour forth their scent, much as does our American skunk when attacked. Attendants remove the secretion from time to time without harming the cats.

J. C. Andersen of New York wrote me that civet arrives

packed in buffalo horns covered with parchment at the top. This safeguards the peculiar smell. Usually 20 to 30 ounces are in a horn, and the price at present is around $7.00 an ounce. Civet helps to round out a perfume's bouquet and is thought to give it a lasting quality.

Musk, however, is more important than civet, castor, or ambergris. Its influence in perfume is subtler, more powerful. As many as seventeen components may enter a single perfume; musk harmonizes and blends these into a single fragrance and makes that fragrance richer and more appealing. Perfumers say that musk "exalts" all other perfume materials. It enhances the perfume-sorcery, imparting to it a "warmth" and "vitality" that no other single substance can.

With 100,000 musk deer slain each year, what is the future of the little animal? It seems incredible that he should have been able to survive the increased demand for perfume. We now have perfumes in shampoos and shaving lotions; perfumes in paints and insecticides; perfumes in beverages, medicines, and foods; perfumes in air-conditioning apparatus that introduce a note of outdoor freshness, and perfumes even on the hides of elephants before they perform in circuses.

Chemists, reviewing the situation, recognized the necessity of synthesizing musk. There was already artificial musk, a workable substitute. Why not, then, actual musk—musk chemically and actively the same as that from the pouch of the little musk deer, but produced in laboratories rather than among the rhododendrons? The scientists succeeded. The result is pure musk, dependable in strength and chemically appraisable, which natural musk is not.

Chemists had already added over 800 substances to the aromatic scale. They had evolved shades for each odor type, gradations as definite as the gradations of colors. They synthesized lilac perfume, even though pure lilac oil, to date, has never been extracted from real lilacs. And they synthesized lily of the valley, a perfume not existing until synthesized. Oil of lemon grass helps in synthesizing violet perfume; oil of geranium and oil of citronella in synthesizing rose. They now have synthetic musk.

Synthetic musk, called "Astrotone" as produced in the Du Pont laboratories, gives the little musk deer in the Himalayas some respite from his hunters. It does not yet replace the musk from 100,000 deer a year. But it is pure, and it costs infinitely less. So the little music-loving deer, could he but know it, would surely welcome this chemical magic that bids fair to prolong his life.

❧ THE ELUSIVE SEA OTTER ❧ *A curious and playful sea mammal whose rare pelt is worth a thousand dollars* ❧ BY ALAN G. MAY.

HAVE YOU ever seen a sea otter at close quarters? Probably not, for there are none on exhibition at any of the zoos or aquariums in this country. Few museums even have a complete skeleton.

The sea otter, *Enhydra lutris* (Linn.), was first discovered in the Aleutian Islands by the early Russian fur hunters. Vitus Bering's ship, the "St. Peter," was wrecked in 1741 on the island now known as Bering Island, on the way back to Kamchatka after his voyage of discovery to America. Here the survivors found many sea otters. These animals at first were unafraid of man, and the shipwrecked crew were able to kill them quite easily with clubs in order to use the meat for food and the pelts for building shelters. On returning to the port of Petropavlovsk after seven months on the island, they took with them over 700 sea otter pelts. The arrival of these furs in Russia led to other expeditions in search of sea otters, and so it was that the animals were discovered to the eastward in the Aleutian Islands. In the mad rush to secure these valuable pelts, the Russians killed both male and female alike, sometimes even the pups. This almost brought about the extermination of the sea otter, as happened to the sea cow by the year 1768.

The adult sea otter is a sleek-looking, playful sea mammal with a flattish head, small ears, long whiskers, and a strong, thick, medium length tail. It has an over-all length of between four and five feet, and weighs from 45 to 70 pounds. The pelts give the appearance of having come from a much larger ani-

81

mal, as the skin hangs in loose folds on the body, and in the process of drying and tanning they stretch considerably.

In color the fur runs from a deep brown to jet black, the under part of the body and neck being of a lighter shade. Often the guard hairs are silver-tipped. The fur is soft, lustrous, and glossy on pelts in prime condition. Sea otters shed their fur at all seasons of the year. The pelts have always had a high value and today are worth approximately $1000 apiece. Naturally, these pelts are extremely rare, for these animals are now protected by the Government. None at all can be killed.

The sea otter lives mainly on crustaceans, mollusks, octopuses, small fish, and seaweed. Because this source of supply is only found close to the shore, the animals are rarely seen far out at sea. Their sense of hearing and their eyesight do not appear to be exceptionally good, but this is offset by their particularly keen power of smell.

Although larger than the land otter, the sea otter has characteristics of its land cousin and also those of the seal. It might be described as an intermediate between the two animals. The rear legs and feet of the sea otter are constructed on much the same plan as the flippers of the seal and resemble a flipper more than a foot. Their front legs and webbed feet are used with great dexterity.

It is an odd fact that these animals also have some human characteristics, demonstrated by many of their actions. The manner in which they use their front legs and feet is one such characteristic, for they use them in the same way we do our hands and arms. A male will caress a female, rubbing cheeks, or "kissing," and using his forefeet as hands in stroking the female. The mother sea otter nurses her pup at her breast in human fashion and also cradles her pup in her "arms" as do human beings. Mother animals have been seen to play with their pup by throwing it into the air and catching it again. One Aleut reported having seen them play with seaweed, tossing it into the air to catch it as it fell.

The early Russian fur hunters stated that a mother would protect her pup with her life. If the pup was killed and the mother escaped, she would return and carry the dead pup with her for many days, later dying of sorrow or a broken heart. On land, the mother carries her pup by the nape of the neck as does a cat her kitten; and when angry, the sea otter hisses like a cat.

Steller, the great naturalist who accompanied Bering, was the first white man to set foot on Alaskan soil. He described the sea otter as ". . . a beautiful, pleasing animal, amusing, and cunning in its habits." He reported that if some of these animals escaped into the sea after being chased by man, they would wave one "arm" in apparent derision at their pursuers. Sometimes they would hold one of their "hands" over their eyes to shade them in order to see better. When watching something from the water, they have the habit of rising vertically so that almost half the body is out of the water.

The molar teeth, with which they crush shellfish, are almost human in appearance, although somewhat larger. At irregular intervals the sea otters will migrate a considerable distance in large or small herds, returning to their own locality after an indefinite period of roaming.

They sleep in the water on their backs with their front legs in the air, jaw resting on chest, and the rear legs or flippers lying in the water to maintain their balance. When sleeping on the rocks of the shore, one of their number acts as guard to warn of any danger. They have few enemies, however; probably only the killer whale and sea lions. In groups or herds they are friendly and amiable creatures, never fighting among themselves. When playing they have a preference to be near large patches of seaweed, into which they dive, remaining under water two to three minutes.

The swimming ability of the sea otter equals that of the seal or is possibly better. It is a real joy to watch these graceful animals sporting in the water. In play they seem to vie with one another in aquatic acrobatics, turning somersaults, rolling over and over like a spinning log, so fast that they appear like a whirling blur.

Apparently, the sea otter pup must be taught to swim. The mother places the pup on her breast and takes to the water on her back, then gently pushes her offspring into the water. When the pup is tired or in difficulty, the mother picks it up and allows it to rest on her breast before repeating the lesson.

The figures on the sea otter herds of the Aleutian Islands are confidential. These herds, while not large at present, show every indication that with the full protection of the Government, they will be steadily increasing year by year. Although sea otters can be seen occasionally on almost any of the Aleutian Islands and also along the coast southward, they frequent two islands in particular. These islands cannot be named, as sea otter poachers still exist. The Japanese knew of one of these islands and are known to have landed there more than once and killed the animals for their pelts.

On Meydni Island, one of the Komandorskie Islands under the jurisdiction of the Republic of Kamchatka, U.S.S.R., there is a little settlement named Gladskuvskaya where the Russians have established the first Sea Otter Experimental Station in the world. It was a great privilege for the writer to be able to visit this station in 1938 when working on an archaeological survey led by Dr. Aleš Hrdlička of the Smithsonian Institution.

Here, with the assistance of a few Aleuts, a Russian biologist was studying these interesting animals and also breeding them in captivity for the first time in history.

Gladskuvskaya was a small settlement of less than a dozen inhabitants, with a few houses and a headquarters building that was used by the biologist as his laboratory and living quarters. Fine looking cattle and hogs roamed at large around the buildings, while the Aleutian Blue Foxes, which were successfully raised on the island, were almost as tame as dogs.

About a half mile from the buildings some large pens had

been erected on a salt-water lake in which the tide rises and falls. In these pens the sea otters were kept segregated.

In order to determine whether the sea otter could live indefinitely in fresh water, one pen had been built in a fresh-water lake near by. Over a century ago Russian fur hunters reported seeing sea otters in inland lakes of the Aleutians, but it was not known whether this was their natural habitat or whether they were visiting there. The animals that we saw in the fresh-water pen appeared to be every bit as active and healthy as those in the salt-water pens.

The scientist in charge of this Experimental Station was assigned to his post for three years. On this bleak, treeless, rocky island, with no other white man for company, it was indeed edifying to find this gentleman so content and gratified with the accomplishment of his task. He was proud of his work and only too happy to show us all he could; however, owing to the language difficulty, it was hard to obtain much information from him.

At the enclosures, the scientist threw a fish to one of the sea otters. The otter deftly caught it in its "hands." Rolling over on its back, it took the head of the fish in one "hand," the tail in the other, and commenced to eat it at leisure in a very dignified manner. Having finished, the sea otter carefully brushed the remnants of the meal off its chest; then, dipping its hands in the water, the animal rubbed them together just as a person does when washing with soap and water. This finished, the creature proceeded to wash its face carefully, even going behind its ears like any human being. Finally, to complete the toilet, the whiskers were brushed off sideways.

A short time before we arrived, one sea otter had had great difficulty in giving birth to her pup. Usually only one pup is born at a time, birth taking place at any time throughout the year. In order to save the life of this mother sea otter, the biologist had had to operate. He was successful in saving the life of the mother, but he was chagrined to lose the pup. Later in his laboratory, he proudly showed us his first attempt at taxidermy—the sea otter pup he had been unable to save.

This experiment at Gladskuvskaya was obviously a most worth-while project and one that might, in a few years' time, succeed in obtaining all the necessary information about this valuable animal. This information in turn may be the fore-runner of a prosperous fur industry. It would seem most likely that in the future the sea otter herds will be maintained and at the same time a certain number taken yearly for their pelts.

Prior to the war, plans were afoot in the United States to place men on one of the Aleutian Islands where the sea otter lives. While studying the animals, these men would also be able to protect them from poachers. Thus it can be imagined that the sea otter will regain sufficient numbers in Aleutian waters to ensure their survival as a part of the animal population of the region.

MORE ABOUT SEA OTTERS

by Edward Weyer, Jr.

Soon after Alaska was acquired by the United States, kill-ing of this unique animal was rigidly curtailed, and in 1910, when the otter seemed doomed, complete protection was given. During the 1940's, a long-range program to increase its numbers was instituted. In 1950 it was reported that there were more than 8000 sea otters in the Aleutians-Alaskan area. These are independent of a small herd that has been rigidly protected by the state of California. In former times, sea otters were found all along the Pacific Coast. The U. S. Fish and Wildlife Service is undertaking to create new colonies through the transplanting of small numbers to favorable areas.

During the early part of this century, about all that the federal agencies could do for the otters was to preserve secrecy about the location of small groups that were known to exist. The agencies did not have the necessary funds for much patrol work. In the 1930's, however, the Navy and Coast Guard gathered evidence indicating that Japanese "fishing craft" might be netting sea otters illegally in Alaskan waters. Indeed, it was the sighting of a Japanese vessel in an inlet of Amchitka Island that started the present management program. The sea-going ship had entered an inlet where no ship could possibly be afloat—according to Navy charts. The charts indicated that the inlet was filled with rocky reefs, which would surely destroy any ship. The Japanese ship, however, on sighting the Navy vessel, put on steam and sailed away, right over the "rocks." Investigations showed that the "rocks" were really rip tides that created an illusion of reefs.

In the inlet was found a large group of sea otters. Hidden away from hunters and pirates, the otters had lived and multiplied for many years. The Bureau of Fisheries then received a small appropriation from Congress for the establishment of a sea otter station on Amchitka. When the Bureau of Fisheries and the Biological Survey were consolidated in 1940 to become the Fish and Wildlife Service, the sea otter management program was given impetus.

During the war years, sea otters began to multiply in their relative security. Now there are about 4000 on Amchitka and about the same number scattered in small groups along other islands and coastal areas.

The Fish and Wildlife Service reports that the sea otter cannot live except along certain shore lines. It needs an area where the water is comparatively shallow, as off shelving beaches. In such localities sea urchins live, upon which the otters feed mainly. There also must be kelp beds, in which the otter can rest, play, and hide from killer whales. Killer whales and man are the sea otter's two worst enemies. The otters are constantly on the alert for them, occasionally shading their eyes from the glare of the sun with their paws to look for the single large fin of a killer whale cutting through the water or to spot man's boats approaching.

The sea otter has so many of the characteristics or mannerisms of people that it is often called the "child of the sea" or "old man of the sea." The two names are not as contradictory as they first appear. While the 55-inch long, 50-pound adult looks like an old man, with grizzly hair on head and shoulders and a full, bristly mustache, it lives and plays like a child. The sea otter undulates through the water with a scissors kick, now and then rolling over on its back to kick itself along with one foot—its forepaws complacently resting on its chest. The sea otter's chest also serves as its table. On it, the otter spreads sea urchins as it tears them apart. While nibbling one tasty bit, the animal is apt to lose another to the floating sea gull that lazily swims about the "table" looking for an unguarded piece of food.

Perhaps with better knowledge of their specialized food habits, it may become possible to keep sea otters alive in captivity. But the attempt must be regarded pessimistically until proved otherwise by careful experimentation. Meanwhile, we shall have to content ourselves with the reports that issue from the scientific custodians of this fabulous little animal.

THE RATTLESNAKE OF THE SEA ✿ *The Sting Ray which haunts many beaches can be avoided. Here's how* ✿ BY CURTIS ZAHN.

THE STORY of the sting ray is handed down, from person to person, bather to bather. Sometimes it is embellished and often it is belittled. Seldom are authoritative statistics divulged. Seaside colonies jealously guard the news, probably feeling that the less said, the better for their clientele. First aid stations admit the presence of *Urobatis halleri* with a fatalistic shrug. They handle dozens of its victims daily in some localities, but their lips are mysteriously sealed. Although millions of bathers know the sting ray as a character of questionable reputation, hundreds make its acquaintance the hard way each season. The wound from its barbed stinger is painful, varying from an easily healing scratch of an hour's discomfort, to one that causes injury for weeks, and in rare cases, death. The result is that many people forego surf bathing entirely, leaving it to uninformed tourists who stride innocently into infested water. Again, there are the fatalists who would wade anyway, taking their chances. The truth of the matter lies somewhere between. It is possible to safely invade the waters of *Urobatis halleri* once one learns about the habits and limitations of this most formidable of flat fishes.

According to David Starr Jordan, the round sting ray was first discovered off San Diego, California, in 1863 and named for a young man who was "stung at the time of the discovery." Undoubtedly the fish was unofficially known before that. The California Indians are said to have used the barbed stingers for arrowheads. This family of *Dasyatidae* is abundant in Asiatic and Australian waters, where natives utilize the dried skins for various purposes. The species is one of the easiest to

find on California coasts, and there is reason to believe that
sting rays are on the increase. The reproductive rate is vast,
one to eight young being hatched "alive and very healthy."
The death rate, on the other hand, is not at all reassuring.
They have few if any enemies. Large fish cannot invade their
shallow water environment. They are inedible and are not
used commercially in any way. Pleasure fishermen avoid them
for obvious reasons.

Urobatis halleri might well be called the rattlesnake of the
sea. This creature is to bathers what the rattler is to hikers.
What it lacks in viciousness, it supplants with its very abun-
dance. And in addition to its scorpion-like defense apparatus,
the sting ray has the ability to become one with its surroundings. All such flat fishes are mud colored, varying only in
shades to match the environment. While corbina, croaker,
perch, and other surf fishes flee from approaching bathers, the
sting ray lies serene and camouflaged. It will often cover itself with silt and refuse to be dislodged from its mudhole.
When the unsuspecting victim places a foot upon its back, the
tail flips up in an arc, burying the stinger usually about the
ankle. Charges have been glibly made that poison is injected
from fangs or sacs. This is not true. The infection results from
an acid slime coating the bone barb. It is undecided whether
the slime gets its toxicity from pollution around bay and sea
bottoms or from the skin of the fish, but certainly it does not
come from an interior source. Treatments vary from hot water
and salts to other medication. The main thing is that the victim
go immediately to a first aid station or a doctor. From this
point on, time is the only healing factor.

Certainly the ray's living habits make it one of the most
unsanitary of all fishes. It feeds on dead or living mud organisms, never taking live minnows or surface baits. It prefers bay
ooze to sandy bottoms and dwells by preference in hot and
stagnant waters. The body structure is fragile. Its mushy soft-
ness is comparable almost to that of a jellyfish. It is incapable

of prolonged activity and spends most of its time resting prone on the bottom. When "flushed," it will dart with an undulating, fluttering gait for a distance of usually but a few feet. Then, skidding to a stop, it becomes enveloped in its own dust, which finally settles over, completely hiding the fish from enemies.

Few victims have ever seen the fish that stung them. The swirling, sandy waters of the surf and muddy bay conditions make it nearly impossible. The round, tapered shape of *Urobatis halleri* makes him fit into the landscape. Often, in six inches of water, the fish remains hidden from the sharpest eye.

Interviews with life guards and first aid workers bear out the theory that rays generally prefer conditions not altogether similar to those desired by swimmers. True, both seem to want warm water. The bather, however, stays away from ooze and slime. Nor does he like the dead and stagnant water of bay shores. If he did, the guards assure us, thousands of people would be stung. For every sting ray in the ocean surf, there are dozens in the bays. Statistics show us that most casualties are suffered in the ocean, but statistics also show that few people wade bay shores whereas millions wade the surf. This same observation applies to the theory that the chances of getting stung in a crowded surf are as great as when bathers are few. Actually the risk is cut down when the bather wades to sea in the midst of hundreds of other splashing bathers. Prolonged activity by people will eventually drive out nearly all sting rays, but they will return shortly after quiet has been restored. Sting rays are commonest at low tide, when beaches are apt to be flat. If the waves break far out, rolling in so that there is always a constant body of water one foot deep or more over a large area, sting rays will be abundant. Add to this, soft sand and warm water and the conditions are ideal.

From the above remarks, it should be obvious that safety in swimming lies in finding the opposite conditions from those enjoyed by the sting ray. High tides, heavy breakers, and coarse sand beaches with steep shores harbor few of them. Cold water plays a part. In winter and early spring, the rays will be concentrated in the warm shallows of bays and sloughs. It is here that they breed and live in their most suitable environment. The ones that frequent ocean environments are, comparatively speaking, the exception.

Yet sting rays are so numerous that despite hundreds of casualties it is safe to assume that the great majority of bathers walk through their territory in safety. Most of the rays dart away from the path of the intruder. The few that cannot be dislodged are stepped upon by unlucky individuals who are victims of the great law of averages.

In order further to cut down chances of injury, there is one more important step. It is the step the bather takes as he walks into waters abounding with *Urobatis halleri*. For if one drags or slides his feet over the bottom, it is nearly impossible to get stung. The ray's sting apparatus is designed in such a way that he cannot inflict a wound unless the victim's foot is over the center portion of the body. Thus, when the wader drags his feet, his toes will strike the side of the resting fish. In any case, this will cause the sting ray to dart off, and the tail carrying the barb will be unable to describe enough arc to touch the foot. It is true that most bathers fail to drag their feet so that the toes dig into the sand. It spoils some of the pleasure and spontaneity of surf sport. Yet, this is an almost infallible way to avoid painful contact. At the same time, stamping or thumping the feet, thus splashing the water violently, helps to drive out the majority of rays.

It has been rumored, from time to time, that people are stung while actually swimming. The writer has never found a case of this kind, nor talked to anyone with proof of its happening. On the occasions when sting rays do swim, they keep within inches of the bottom. Besides this, they are more alert when away from the protection of mud, and more wary.

Another point is that they cannot get enough leverage when swimming to drive the stinger sufficiently hard.

The many kinds of rays range from the round sting ray, averaging six inches in diameter, to the manta ray with a spread of 25 feet. There are the skates and eagle rays and various cousins, all related to and descended from the sharks. There is even the guitar fish, which resembles these flat fishes in design and habits. Yet, only two California rays are dangerous. The small round sting ray and the rat-tailed sting ray are the only ones able to use their stingers. Both are round as saucers. The rat-tailed sting ray differs in its large size (often being two to four feet in diameter) and in its whiplike tail, which attains a length surpassing that of the fish. The rat-tailed sting ray is rare, however, and frequents deeper water. It is also more difficult to approach than the smaller species.

Urobatis halleri, the rattlesnake of the sea, is most to be feared. He can drive his barb to the bone. But if the individual learns the sting ray's habits and watches his step, he will not have to make the creature's acquaintance the hard way.

THE WELL-TRAVELED EEL ✤ *The amazing voyages of European and American Eels from their birthplace in the Sargasso Sea* ✤ BY PAUL BULLA.

OFF THE North American continent, southeast of Bermuda and northeast of Puerto Rico, lies a vast tract of slowly swirling water known to mariners as the Sargasso Sea. Here, according to song and story, the Gulf Stream is born, and here far below the weed-choked surface is the breeding and spawning grounds of our fresh-water eel.

Here these strange fish have their rendezvous. In this sea-within-a-sea they are born, and here, after years spent in far places, they return to reproduce themselves and die, for no spent eels have ever been seen, and adult eels have never been known to run upstream.

Of all the fish known to mankind, few have a more remarkable life history, and none have puzzled scientists for so long as have these snake-like denizens of the rivers and lakes of Europe and America. Down through the ages they have been a food delicacy in the European and Mediterranean countries, but centuries passed before their migratory habits and method of propagation were explained. Each autumn uncounted numbers of these slimy creatures moved downstream to the sea, where many were caught in the nets of fishermen awaiting their migration. But great numbers avoided this fate and disappeared never to return.

In the spring and summer of each succeeding year, tiny eel-like creatures appeared from somewhere in the vast ocean spaces and swarmed along the coast of Europe and through the Straits of Gibraltar into the Mediterranean. Later they entered the fresh-water streams and rivers that ran down to the sea, penetrating to the interior, where they grew to maturity. Confusion further confounded the minds of scientists and simple fisherfolk alike by the fact that eggs of unborn eels were never found in the bodies of adults, and males of the species were never seen.

Many strange theories were advanced in explanation of how they were produced, ranging from spontaneous generation to the transformation of horsehairs into little eels. Aristotle, in the fourth century B.C., held that eels were born from earthworms, which were in turn produced from mud or damp soil. The early Greeks, failing to find spawn or male reproductive glands within the eels, named Jupiter as the father, as all children of doubtful parentage were ascribed to this god.

Pliny the Elder, great Roman naturalist and author, declared with conviction that eels had neither masculine nor feminine sex. In accounting for their multiplication, he concluded that they rubbed themselves against rocks, and the pieces scraped from their bodies came to life as little eels. He dismissed the subject as a matter for further controversy with the laconic statement that "they have no other mode of procreation." With the acceptance of such beliefs it is small wonder that centuries elapsed before such theories were dispelled and such superstitions overcome.

It was not until 1777 that the ovary of the eel was first recognized by Carlo Mundini, a professor of anatomy at the University of Bologna, thus definitely establishing a female sex. Ninety-five years later Reinhold Hornbaum-Hornschuch announced the discovery of a male individual. The enigma that had endured for over 2000 years was then on its way to being solved.

But while these discoveries partly answered the riddle of their existence, where the eels came from and how they were produced still remained a mystery. It was left to a German named Johann Jakob Kaup, in 1846, to find in the sea a small ribbonlike fish with a tiny head. Curious as to its species, he took it home and placed it in a bottle of alcohol. After labeling it *Leptocephalus brevirostris,* a name that exceeded the length of the specimen itself, he left it there to be forgotten.

Half a century passed before the subject emerged from the obscurity into which it had been relegated. On a day in 1896 two Italians, Gracci and Calandrucci, found one of Kaup's little fish in the Mediterranean, but one much larger and more fully developed. This they identified as the leptocephalus or larva of the edible eel that inhabited the streams of the European continent. With that beginning the stage was set for a Danish scientist named Johannes Schmidt.

As director of the Danish Commission for the Exploration of the Sea, Schmidt sailed in 1906, on the first of many subsequent expeditions, to locate the breeding and spawning grounds of this specter of the deep. For fifteen years he towed nets up and down the Atlantic, taking specimens of leptocephali from the English Channel to Chesapeake Bay, and from Greenland to Puerto Rico. Over this vast area he collected and correlated sizes of eel larvae, carefully noting the latitude and longitude in which they were obtained.

He reasoned that the larvae were growing as they moved from the place in which they were spawned toward the coast and their fresh-water homes. It followed, therefore, that the smaller the larva found in any part of the ocean, the nearer such specimen must be to the place where it was born. After years of tireless effort he was able, through this method, to fix the breeding and spawning grounds of the European eel (*Anguilla vulgaris*) and the American species (*Anguilla rostrata*) within the latitudes 20 to 30 degrees north, and longitudes 60 to 78 degrees west. He further established the fact that the European beds overlapped those of the American species.

But this discovery uncovered but one phase of the life cycle of the eel. During the period of growth in the waters of their home continent, both males and females are a uniform green to yellowish-brown above, shading to a pale dirty white under-

Scarcely 20 inches tall at the shoulders, the little Musk Deer has no antlers but shows two curving teeth, projecting from the upper jaw. Near the base of his abdomen is a walnut-size pouch containing such a valuable essence that his life is in constant peril.

(*See page 73.*)

U. S. Fish and Wildlife Service, Photo by Warden Carl Lo

The adult Sea Otter looks like an old man, with grizzly hair and bristly mustache, but it lives and plays like a child. At maturity, it is 55 inches long and weighs 50 pounds.

(*See page 81.*)

The migration of American eels is shown by the dotted lines, that of European eels by the white bars.

(*See page 94.*)

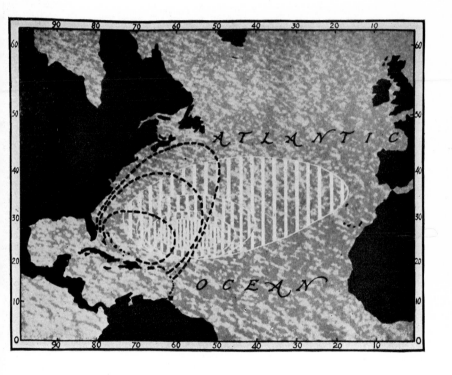

Photo by Woody Williams, courtesy Steinhart Aquarium
California Academy of Sciences, San Francisco

Bright orange with conspicuous white stripes, the Clown Fish attracts much attention in the aquarium because of its beautiful appearance. But its extraordinary habits are even more startling.

(*See page 103.*)

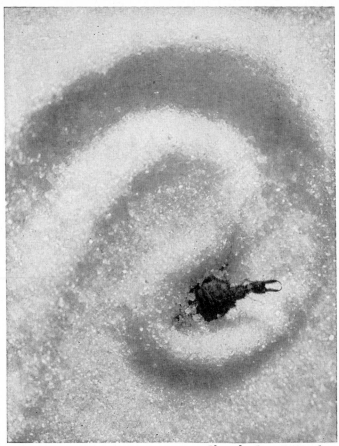

The Ant Lion begins by making a circle and then continuing to work toward the center, tossing sand out with its head and jaws. It then conceals itself at the bottom and waits for whatever fortune may bring. Ant Lions have been known to live at the bottom of their pitfall for three years waiting for prey.

(*See page 107.*)

Photo by Ross E. Hutch

An ant comes near the edge. The soft sugar, which has been used in place of sand, begins to give way, and the Ant Lion begins to toss particles into the air to knock the ant in.

(*See page 107.*)

This huge insect is a true fly of the genus Pantophthalmus. Attention is directed to the balancing organs or "halteres," just behind the base of the wings. On top of the head between the separated compound eyes are seen the three simple eyes that are found in a number of fly families.

(*See page 111.*)

American Museum of Natural History photo

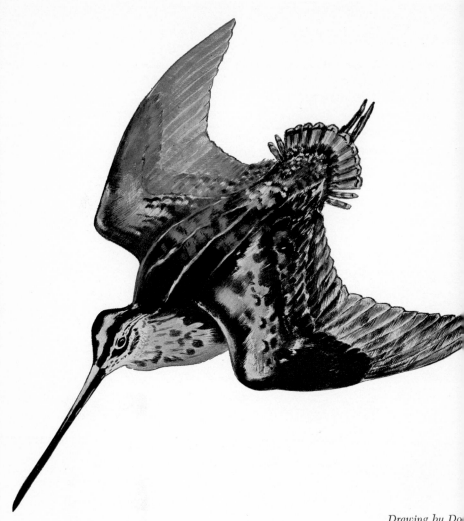

From the "wide blue yonder" comes a soft, haunting cadence as the Jacksnipe dives earthward toward its mate.

(*See page 113.*)

neath, and are called "yellow eels." When the migratory instinct asserts itself at the breeding stage, which is in the autumn when they are between the ages of seven and fifteen years, the sides of their bodies take on a metallic sheen and their backs become a deep black. This is their breeding dress, and they are then known as "silver eels."

Upon assuming this dress, certain other marked changes take place in the females. Their snouts become sharp, the eyes larger, and the pectoral fins, just back of the gill slits, more pointed than usual. Although they have been voracious eaters all their lives, they cease feeding at this time and, leaving the lakes and rivers in which they have lived, move downstream to the sea. But while these visible changes have been taking place, it is not until after they have reached salt water that the ovaries mature. In fact, no perfectly ripe female eel and only one ripe male has ever been seen. Upon arriving in the bays and estuaries of their home shores they are joined by the mature males that have been living there, and together they start the journey back to their birthplace, over 2500 miles distant.

It is not known how far below the surface they swim, but somewhere beyond the continental shelf they pass from the range of observation. Neither is it known how long it takes them to reach their destination, but it has been estimated that the eel requires about six months to make the crossing, swimming at the rate of one-half mile an hour. As the migration from the European continent begins in early autumn, and spawning starts in early spring at the breeding grounds, this estimate of the period of time for the trip seems to be justified.

Upon arrival at the breeding grounds, the European species find they must share it with their American cousins, whose beds overlap their own but extend westward from it. From Labrador southward to Panama and the West Indies, the "silver eels" from America have journeyed to the rendezvous in from one to two months after reaching salt water. Hundreds of fathoms below the seaweed-clogged surface of this tropical sea the eggs of both species are spawned; the females producing from five to 20 million tiny eggs, transparent and almost colorless.

Spawning begins in late winter or early spring, and a week or so after fertilization the eggs are hatched. Larvae of both species begin life with a length of about one-fourth inch. Ribbonlike in shape and so transparent that newsprint can be read through their bodies, they float for a time from 600 to 900 feet below the surface. Later they rise into the upper layers of water and slowly move northward. Reaching the latitude of Bermuda, a separation occurs. The larvae of the European species move eastward on the long journey back to their native shores, while their tiny American relatives turn toward the coast line of America.

During their first summer of life, the European larvae are found in the western Atlantic. By the second summer they have reached the central Atlantic, and by the third they have arrived off the coastal banks of Europe. During their two and one-half years in the ocean they have attained a length of two to three and one-half inches, but they still retain their flat, leaf-shaped larval form. They are now faced with a new way of life and must be prepared to meet it. In the course of the autumn and winter a metamorphosis takes place. They cease feeding, lose their larval teeth, shrink in depth and length, and become elvers, or little eels. While they are shaped like their parents in miniature, they are still transparent, and so are known as "glass eels."

Our American eel has a shorter larval history. Here again the timing is perfect, for it reaches its home shores and the elver stage of existence in about one year.

After the transformation from larva to elver, the females of both species ascend the fresh-water streams of their "native" land to live their lives in the interior, until the moment when the migratory instinct drives them back to the sea. In these journeys upstream they use pipe lines and sewers and clamber over falls and surmount dams to reach their destination. The males, however, remain in the brackish waters of lagoons and estuaries, where they grow to maturity and await the down-stream migration of the females.

As eels have been found in ponds having no outlets or inlets, it is believed (though without conclusive evidence) that they will travel overland to reach these oases, choosing nights when the grass is damp for the journey. They are also at home in high as well as low altitudes, having been found in Swiss lakes 3000 feet above sea level.

All eels in the headwaters of large streams are found to be females. As a rule they lie buried by day in the muddy bottoms where there is still water, and venture abroad to feed at night. Being scavengers and omnivorous, they will eat almost any available food, either living or dead. They have even been known to eat their own kind.

Female eels average from two to three and one-half feet in length, but they have been known to reach four feet and weigh as much as sixteen and one-half pounds. Males average around fourteen to eighteen inches in length, but never grow larger than two feet. The vertebrae of this fish mark the only difference between the American and the European species: the former have an average of 107 segments, while the latter averages 114.

Differing from their salt-water cousins, the lower jaw of both species projects beyond the upper, while the large mouth gapes back to a point even with or somewhat behind the eyes. On the side of the neck are gill slits with upper corners on a line with the center of the base of the pectoral fins. A single fin, soft and without spines, extends along the back, around the tip of the tail, and forward on the underside of the body. There is no separation into dorsal, caudal, or anal parts. After the third or fourth year of life, eels develop small scales that are embedded in the skin. These are covered with a coating of slimy mucus, which has given rise to the simile, "as slippery as an eel."

Perhaps the most intriguing phase of the life cycle of this unusual fish is that neither European nor American elvers have ever been known to appear off the shores of any country but their own. This fact immediately presents two puzzling questions that challenge the imagination.

1. What causes the immature larvae of the European species to move eastward from the spawning grounds, while its American cousin works toward the west side of the Atlantic?

2. How does it happen that the timing is perfect for both species to reach the elver stage within a few months after arriving off the coast of their home continent?

These questions may be answered in part by the difference in their individual larval histories.

While the European larva requires from two and one-half to three years to reach the elver stage of development after life begins, the larval stage of the American species is terminated in about one year. This time element not only acts to keep the two species distinct, but makes it practically impossible for either to survive in waters other than their own after metamorphosis takes place. Should the larvae of the European eels, for instance, move westward, they would reach the American coast line still in an undeveloped larval stage.

A geographical cause for their distribution is advanced by Doctor Schmidt, who points out that the center of production for the American eel lies farther west and south than the center of the European beds. This, together with the movement of the ocean currents as an aid to the journey in the early stages of larval development, must be considered as a cause directing the two species each to its own side of the ocean.

While much has been learned of the habits of these sluggish, sedentary fish since the turn of the century, much remains unexplained.

With a singleness of purpose and an unerring instinct that

has confused scientists, untold thousands have deserted their home waters each autumn to seek adventure in a tropic sea and to keep their rendezvous with death. Weak and immature, their progeny is cast adrift far from their native land. Unguided, these feeble swimmers travel a road over which they have never journeyed, to reach their home continent.

Truly, the eel is one of the greatest of marine mysteries.

❧ LIVING ON BORROWED AIR ❧ BY ROY L. ABBOTT ❧ PROFESSOR OF BIOLOGY, IOWA STATE TEACHER'S COLLEGE.

WHILE many kinds of air-breathing animals have learned to go under water for various purposes and for varying periods of time, it is to the water spider that we must turn for real perfection in this ancient diving game. She can stay under water for hours and days—even sleeps and raises her young down there. How does she manage to stay under so long? By a method almost too novel to be believed.

First of all, she spins a broad airproof web down under the water, fastening it at each end between the stems of water plants. This web is to be her living quarters and must be filled with fresh air from above. How? Madam Spider knows. When her web is properly anchored, she comes to the surface, thrusts her hinder parts and back legs into the air with a kind of clutching motion, then drags them quickly under again, thus catching a bubble of air on her hairy legs and body. Next, down she goes to the web and, coming up from beneath, releases her bubble of air, which remains under the web. Then back to the surface she travels for another. As the amount of air increases, its buoyancy lifts the elastic and loosely stretched web into a kind of sac closed at the top and open at the bottom. Into this magic chamber Madam Spider crawls and remains as long as her air supply lasts, even hanging her eggs there from its ceiling. Eventually, however, when her air supply becomes vitiated, she cuts a hole in the top to allow it to escape, finally repairing and refilling the chamber for further use.

Has this queen of divers left anything to us by way of originality in going under the water?

🌿 THE CLOWN FISH AND THE ANEMONE 🌿

A strange partnership in nature 🌿 BY WOODY WILLIAMS.

IT IS not uncommon for an aquarist to be accused of touching up his tropical fish with a paintbrush—especially if the fish are damselfishes (Pomacentrids), such as *Amphiprion percula*. These pygmy beauties, about three inches long, are bright orange with bizarre stripes of white, and their fins are tipped with black. They come from the Indo-Australian coral reefs of the western Pacific. Because of their slow, clumsy "gait" and flamboyant color patterns they have been named "clown fish." But to the biologist they are more than comical oddities from the South Seas. As partners of the large sea anemones, they represent one of nature's most astounding examples of symbiosis—the close association of two dissimilar organisms for mutual benefit.

Symbiosis is not rare in nature, but there are few examples where the relationship seems so intimately integrated as among the damselfishes and the large sea anemones, such as *Stoichactes*, among whose tentacles they make their home.

These petal-like tentacles, to all appearance as innocent as a daisy, actually possess the stinging power of a nest of hornets. Some of the tropical anemones are known to inflict painful wounds on man, to say nothing of their potency against lower creatures of the sea. The instrument that produces such effective results is a comparatively complicated one-celled structure called a nematocyst, present in countless numbers. These stinging cells eject a dart which, when it pierces the tissue of an unlucky visitor, injects a poison that often causes pain or death. Yet the damselfish nestles among these lethal tentacles with perfect safety. Indeed, the fish's very existence

103

on the reef would be questionable if it were not able to seek refuge among the anemones without bodily harm. If deprived of its hiding place, it would become an easy prey to larger forms, for it is a slow swimmer and it has a gaudy appearance.

Apparently these fishes are immune to the poison of the stinging cells. But not just any anemone with an effective battery satisfies a given species of damselfish. Each kind of damselfish restricts itself to one or sometimes a few species of anemones, the choice depending probably to some extent on appropriate size. The marine biologists in Java who have studied *Amphiprion* and related forms most extensively have learned to predict which species of damselfish will be found in given types of sea anemones.

They have also found that damselfishes are primarily individualists. Once a pair of clown fish have established a home in an anemone (or a group of anemones), they tend to maintain the territory for themselves. However, young clown fish are sometimes found in the same anemones with adults, who perhaps did not have the persuasive power to evict the youngsters.

Some relatives of the clown fish are quite emphatic in their defense of home. This trait sometimes leads to their capture. When a diver descends near their home, they will rush out from the anemone and nip his legs, shoes, and net, thus exposing themselves to easy capture. Generally, however, the clown fish will hide in the disc of the anemone, remaining there even after the anemone is lifted from the water, and in this way they can be collected. Such a clown fish, together with its anemone, lived for years under the care of a woman in Philadelphia, according to Frederick H. Stoye, who writes on tropical aquarium fishes.

The species of *Amphiprion* illustrated in this book is believed to pair off for life. The female outdoes the male in size, and following a tendency that some think they detect in human society, she is the agressive suitor. Nipping each other's flanks is one of the favorite courtship pastimes. The male cleans off a hard surface at the base of the anemone, and the female deposits 200 or 300 eggs. The housekeeping is done by the male. After the eggs have been laid, he rubs against the tentacles of the anemone, directing them downward so that they camouflage the eggs. This ability of the clown fish to direct the actions of the anemone is one of the most remarkable aspects of their relationship.

Many details in the later development of the young *Amphiprion* are still concealed in the mystery of reef life. However, the Netherlands scientists are quite certain that after hatching, the young swim to the surface and feed on tiny floating or weakly swimming animals. Many *Amphiprion*, in turn, are of course preyed upon by larger creatures in this combination nursery and hunting ground at the surface of the sea.

In a short time, the survivors of this vertical migration drop again to the bottom and search out anemones in which to set up housekeeping. If the anemones are scarce, several clown fish may congregate in one.

For a time, the clown fish feeds on minute bits of life captured by the tentacles of the sea anemone. But as it matures, it probably again depends primarily on floating organisms passing near its home. In captivity, *Amphiprion* appears to do well on *Artemia*, otherwise known as brine shrimp, which are collected from highly salty waters or hatched out from eggs in salt solutions in the laboratory or home. In nature, the clown fish's feeding habits are not well known.

One species of damselfish is known to carry morsels of food to its anemone and place them among the tentacles. Even more astonishing is the report that a damselfish has been seen to "nurse" a sick anemone back to health by fanning it and rubbing against it, a situation that is said to occur when the sea water becomes unfavorable to the anemone's health. The anemones seem definitely to do better when accompanied by their damselfish. On the other hand, damselfish have occasionally been observed to feed on the tentacles of the anemone that shelters them, and it has been suggested that this habit builds up an immunity to the poison.

Such, in brief, is the strange partnership between these two fascinating animals that dwell together on the bottom of the sea. The average man, lacking the elaborate equipment used by the undersea explorer, can nevertheless observe their strange behavior in some of our public aquaria. One cannot fail to imagine what fascination they would hold as household pets in the home fish tank. But these are creatures of the sea, not of fresh water. Last year, two shipments of *Amphiprion* came into the United States through San Francisco, but the great losses that were suffered in transit across the Pacific caused further efforts toward importation to be dropped. So the best thing one can do is to ask whether he can see the clown fish and its strange partner the next time he visits a large city aquarium.

❧ THE ANT LION'S TRAP ❧ *It's a long time between meals, but the ant lion has plenty of patience* ❧ BY ROSS E. HUTCHINS, ENTOMOLOGIST, STATE PLANT BOARD OF MISSISSIPPI.

IN NATURE there are many ways of making a living, just as there are with human beings, but some of the methods that animals have invented are far stranger than fiction. Take the case of the ant lion. Who would believe it possible that any creature could live and grow fat merely by excavating a pit in the sand and hiding in the bottom? Yet, this is the established way of life for the ant lion.

Almost everyone has seen the tiny pitfalls of these interesting creatures in dry sandy or dusty places, but few know much about the insects themselves.

In the first place, an ant lion has plenty of time. If it hadn't, its way of life would not work. It often has to wait a long time between meals, but it is well adapted to such vicissitudes.

To start at the beginning, the ant lion is a small insect approximately a third of an inch long, with six weak legs and a small head with two sickle-like jaws extending forward. One of the first things one notices about the ant lion is that it can walk only backward, and this is the mode of progression it employs in excavating its small pitfalls. When it has selected a site that seems to offer advantages from the standpoint of the ant lion, it begins to back through the sand, at the same time tossing the sand into the air by flipping its head upward. This process of backing into the sand until it is nearly covered and then tossing the sand out with its head continues in an ever-narrowing circle; and when the center is reached, a neat pit has been formed with nicely sloping sides.

Now, as often happens, the spot at which the ant lion chooses to dig may have a good many small pebbles mixed with the fine sand. This poses a problem to the pit digger but one that it can handle. The method that the ant lion uses to remove pebbles too large to be tossed out with its head was described by a French entomologist in the early 1800's but was questioned by later scientists until careful experiments were made in 1907 by H. C. McCook, whose observations follow: "Three pebbles, all larger and heavier than the ant lion, were dropped into the centre of a pit where they would be most inconvenient to the occupant and likely to prompt her to remove them. The ant lion thrust its head beneath a pebble and tried to toss it from the pit. Having failed in this, it tried another mode. It placed the end of its abdomen against and a little beneath a pebble and began to push backward. A little time was taken to adjust the pebble so that its centre of gravity would be against the end of the body. Then the animal began to back up out of the pit. All of the three pebbles were thus removed." Thus, the correctness of the early observations was confirmed.

These pitfalls vary with the size of the occupant, but they probably average about two inches across and perhaps half that in depth. When completed, the pit is round with smooth sides; and the ant lion then takes up its position concealed in the sand at the bottom.

It waits.

An hour passes, a day passes, perhaps many days pass. Just how long the insect can wait is not known, but eventually its patient vigil pays off. An ant or other small creature wandering about accidentally falls into the pit. It tries desperately to climb out, but the shifting sand makes escape difficult. After a mad scramble, it seems almost on the verge of escape when the ant lion begins tossing sand into the air. With the falling sand overhead and the shifting sand below, the luckless creature suddenly finds itself tumbling to the bottom of the pit. Before it can recover its footing, it is seized by the sickle-like jaws of the ant lion. These jaws are really hypodermic needles, and within a few seconds the captive is killed by the injection of a powerful toxin.

This toxin serves two purposes. In the first place it quickly kills the victim, and in the second place it has the remarkable power to digest or dissolve the body contents of the prey. Of course, this takes time but, as usual, the ant lion is in no hurry. It pulls its booty out of sight under the sand at the bottom of the pit and waits for the poison to do its work. After a time, it begins to suck the nutritious juices through the same hollow jaws into its own stomach, until all that remains of its erstwhile prey is a shriveled carcass, which it tosses out of the pit.

Among the other "believe it or not" characteristics of the ant lion is the fact that the intestinal canal is incomplete. In other words, this insect voids no excrement during the stage of its life that is spent in the pitfall. Another interesting thing is its ability to "play 'possum." If you pick one up with a pair of tweezers, it will usually appear to lose all signs of life, but when placed back on the ground, it will soon "come to life" again and go on about its business.

The life cycle of the ant lion is much longer than that of most insects, owing to the intermittent nature of its food supply. It probably requires from two to three years to reach the adult stage. During this period many vicissitudes may overtake it, and it may move its pitfall many times. The ant lion illustrated elsewhere in this book was collected in an area that is under floodwater to a depth of several feet each winter. Yet when the waters recede and warm weather returns, there are the tiny pits set up for business as usual. Truly, nature takes care of her children.

When, in spite of the irregularity of meals, the ant lion becomes a full-grown larva and is ready to transform to the winged form, it is faced with further complications. When the average caterpillar or other larva spins its cocoon, it merely goes to work weaving silk about itself.

But the ant lion is under fine shifting sand, and if it did not use a special technique, its cocoon would contain not only itself but a lot of sand. If you examine the cocoon of an ant lion with a hand lens, you will see that there is no sand *inside*. The secret was exposed in 1884 in Germany by Redtenbacher, who says, "The larva while spinning lies on its back with its abdomen curved ventrally and, while the sticky thread is issuing, moves the spinneret about in circular, spiral, and confusedly irregular paths. Since the sand grains are thus cemented together by the sticky strands, there arises a confused band of sand, which is gradually consolidated to form a hemisphere . . . Later it turns over and the lower hemisphere is completed and attached to the upper one." Thus the creature builds a cocoon without getting sand inside. Within this cocoon, buried in the sand, the larva transforms into the pupal stage, and for nearly two months it remains in the "sleep of transformation."

One day, however, the side of the cocoon splits open, and the pupal ant lion pushes itself to the surface of the sand. Its skin ruptures along its back, and out comes a bedraggled creature. At first it is pale and delicate, but within a few hours its integument hardens and the limp and crumpled wings expand into transparent, gauzy membranes that carry the transformed creature high over the sands where it had its humble beginning. The lowly, ugly creature that was only a third of an inch long has transformed into a winged adult approximately three inches across and somewhat like a dragon fly in general appearance.

After her years at the bottom of a pitfall, the female has only a limited time, a few days, in which to mate and return to the sand to lay her eggs. Like an insect Cinderella, her period of gaiety is quite short.

🦋 GIANT FLY 🦋 *This titan of the Peruvian jungle has a wingspread of three inches!* 🦋 BY JOHN C. PALLISTER, RESEARCH ASSOCIATE, DEPARTMENT OF INSECTS AND SPIDERS, AMERICAN MUSEUM OF NATURAL HISTORY.

IN THE great Amazonian Basin and extending into the forests of Central America, the West Indies, and even Paraguay is an unusual family of flies known as the Pantophthalmidae. Some of the largest known flies belong to this group. About twenty-five species of them are known, and they resemble giant horseflies. Nearly all are attractively marked with gray and black stripes; the wings are mottled, and the abdomen is frequently banded with or colored a conspicuous red.

An illustration in this book shows one of them procured on a recent entomological expedition of the American Museum of Natural History in the tropical jungles of Peru near the little village of Tingo Maria.

The wanderer in the jungle will occasionally see one of these flies resting in a spot of sunshine on the trunk of a tree or on the leaves of some forest shrub. They are very wary, however, and when you approach one of them, it takes off with a terrific *whr-r-r*. The eye can scarcely follow it as it circles for a moment overhead and then is lost in the treetops. It is this wariness that makes these flies difficult to capture, and the insect collector has to stalk them with patience and dexterity. Probably this is why they are not very abundant in insect collections even in the large museums.

Each fly appears to select an individual territory which it patrols. It rests upon some convenient perch ready to dash forth and drive away any passing insects, apparently in a spirit of sport. The adult flies, from what we know of the life his-

111

tories of a few of the species, apparently do not eat anything, because their mouth parts are atrophied.

The female is known to insert her eggs into crevices in the bark of trees by means of the long ovipositor. When the larvae hatch, they bore into the trunk of the living tree, which is quite unusual for fly larvae. They apparently feed upon the sap as they bore. There seems to be some evidence that the larvae of some species require more than one season to reach maturity.

When full-grown, they work their way out to the surface, pupating at the exit of the burrow.

🎏 THE JACKSNIPE'S WING-SONG 🎏 *A bird that* "*sings*" *without a voice* 🎏 BY BEN EAST.

THERE are few American outdoorsmen who are unfamiliar with the Wilson Snipe. Although this long-billed shore bird has been on the closed list in recent autumns as a result of a marked decline in numbers, he was for a long time a favorite target of marsh gunners. Wherever shotgun addicts meet, he is known and discussed under the name of jacksnipe and admired for his twisting, zigzag flight and for the role he once played on the dun autumn marshlands. Birdmen know him, too.

A. C. Bent, in his *Life History of North American Shore Birds,* ventures the opinion that more snipe have been shot by hunters than any other of the clan, and to prove his point, he cites a kill of 69,000 by one gunner in Louisiana from 1867 to 1887.

Yet surprisingly few persons, either sportsmen or nature lovers, know that this erratic gamester utters one of the strangest, sweetest, and most eerie courtship songs of the bird world. Or perhaps it is hardly accurate to use the word "song," since the jacksnipe's music, made on the wing, is strictly instrumental.

Country school children know this queer wing-song well. Farmers hear it as they widen the brown strips of plowed land across their fields. All who are afield in marsh country in the warm, still days of late April and May have listened to it. But few can identify and name the maker of the high, far-off music.

The Wilson Snipe has no power to sing. His vocal accomplishments are limited to the sharp "*scaip! scaip!*" of alarm he utters when he rises out of the wet sedges ahead of the hunter in autumn and to a few notes of curiosity or protest heard on his nesting grounds. True song is beyond him.

As he moves north on the spring migration with his breeding season near at hand, he mounts high into the sky, far above the green-and-brown checkerboard of fields and woods and marshes. There he circles hour after hour, and every few seconds he interrupts his level circling to dip sharply down like a tiny, feathered dive bomber peeling off for an attack.

It is on this downward dive that he beats out the strange, pulsing notes known to birdmen as winnowing. Authorities did not at first agree as to how he did it. And it might seem impossible to find out, for the snipe sounds his courtship serenade far aloft, in the lonely solitude of the "wide blue yonder," far from man's eyes. But ever since 1858 European scientists have been observing the common European snipe and experimenting to find the secret.

Manson-Bahr mounted the outer tail feathers on a cork attached to a string and rod, and by whirling this contrivance he made an almost perfect imitation of the music. Another experimenter showed that the tremolo effect was added by the vibration of the snipe's wings, which produced certain overtones modifying the music of the tail quills. The sound produced by the American subspecies is described as slightly different in timbre from that of the European snipes, but there is no doubt that the mechanism is the same in both.

The wing-song has, to humans on the ground far below, the quality of a far-off, soft whistle, broken into short syllables, pulsing with a haunting cadence. It floats earthward like the music of a spirit bird.

The first time you stand beside a strip of greening marsh on a windless May morning and listen to the distant "*hoo-hoo-hoo-hoo-hoo-hoo*" coming down from the sky at regular intervals, you are likely to be puzzled about the identity and the location of the musician. But if you search the heavens carefully, sooner or later you will locate the bird—no more than a black speck in the distance—wheeling in swift, wide circles. In a few seconds you will see him dip sharply, and then, after the space of time needed for the sound to travel down to you, you will hear again the sweet notes of the winnow.

At the end of the dip the snipe zooms back to his original altitude and resumes level flight once more, only to dip suddenly earthward again as if to gain the speed necessary for the production of his wing-song.

He keeps it up for hours at a time, doubtless to the delight and satisfaction of the shy hen snipe waiting somewhere in the boglands below. Even to human ears, spring has no bird note more unusual and mystic.

🦋 THE FATAL MRS. MANTIS 🦋 *This Borgia of the insect world is quite at home in the garden* 🦋 BY EDITH FARRINGTON JOHNSTON.

"WHAT *is* that horrible-looking creature?"

This is a question I am asked many times every year between August and November.

The horrible-looking creature is the praying mantis. Even before she goes into action, the female mantis, with her great size, large dull eyes, long angular legs, and spiked and serrated arms, may well stop the beholder in his tracks.

During her early life, from May to August, she is so slender and so much like the green vegetation she inhabits that she is almost never seen. East Indian natives believe that she starts as a small shoot on a plant and first achieves a life of her own in autumn, when she is full-grown. But once her life history is understood, it is fairly easy to find her by searching in the right sort of spot, even in early summer.

In the United States several species of mantises[1] are common. However, the one most frequently noted and collected is the Chinese form, *Paratenodera sinensis*. Its egg masses were accidentally introduced into the United States on nursery stock from the Orient in 1896. Since then it has become thoroughly naturalized and has increased and multiplied. It is one of the most useful of insects, devouring vast numbers of grasshoppers, crickets, cicadas, wasps, and even large spiny or hairy

[1] When speaking of more than one praying mantis you can say mantises, mantes, or mantids. All mantises belong to the family Mantidae, and for this reason scientists generally prefer to call them mantids rather than mantises. The word *Mantis* designates a particular genus of mantids. *Mantis religiosa*, for example, is the common European form. However, popular usage has favored "mantis" and "mantises" as general terms.—ED.

caterpillars. It has gained such a reputation as a benefactor of gardens that in some localities enterprising small boys have collected considerable numbers of the egg masses to sell to amateur gardeners.

The insect catches the attention of the layman not only because of its size, peculiar structure, and its custom of perching on penthouse porches, railway station ramps, or city fire hydrants, but also because it is often noticeably colored. Entomologists tell us that, just as dark or drab-colored creatures sometimes exhibit albino forms, green or greenish insects often produce individuals of varying degrees of pinkness. Sometimes this variation takes the form of a mere shadowing of brown on legs and wings, the chromatic result of spreading pink over green. Frequently the pink has almost superseded the green on abdomen, underwings, and thighs, leaving them a true pink but qualified by the residual green to a shade known to fashionwriters as "dusty pink." And occasionally nature discards all prudence and releases to a hungry world a veritable rose-colored katydid or grasshopper or mantis, doomed, one would think, to an early death by its contrast with its green habitat. Oddly enough, many Chinese mantises with pink abdomen and underwings are captured every year—after they have survived to full maturity! Their escape from enemies can probably be explained by the fact that, except in moments of agitation, the gauzy pink underwings are folded out of sight under the leaf-brown wing covers with their birch-green edges, and the rosy abdomen is visible only from below.

The female particularly has gained the reputation of being fierce and carnivorous, but you need not believe stories that the male contents himself with vegetable food alone, for he is just as carnivorous as the female. I have raised many young mantises straight from the egg case, feeding them on fruit flies; and I have never seen any of them discriminate against the meat diet. At the same time, if you want any males to grow up, you must isolate them at a very tender age, else they will fall victim to the cannibalistic tendencies of the females.

The female, as she matures, and particularly when she is heavy with eggs, develops a feral voracity and an ability to satisfy it, which make her a menace to all insect life. The curious thing is that insects never seem to fear her or to make any effort to escape her advances. The katydid, the butterfly, the mask-faced grasshopper, and the cricket all seem to accept her as a fellow insect and to have no suspicion of her evil designs upon them.

On a grassy bank one late autumn day I saw an endless tapestry of insects, interwoven with brambles, belated butter-'n-eggs, faded grasses, dwarfish goldenrod, asters, and red clover. The theme of the weaving was the hunt of the mantises for their prey, its capture and ingestion. But here was no swift action, no wild panic and pursuit. Like actors in a slow-motion film, the prey crept gently among the slanted weeds, too little warmed by the waning sun to run or leap, while the carnivorous huntresses, whose meat diet better fortified them against the encroaching chill, stalked and consumed them without haste or animosity.

Among her own kind, the female is not at all deterred by ties of kinship from eating her own siblings. Even at mating time, when a certain tenderness might be expected to prevail, she will turn her mournful head backward, bite off her husband's head, and absent-mindedly start munching along down his thorax while he is in the very act of giving life to her 300 eggs!

The female mantis usually appears to be without fear. She is ready to do battle with any foe, from insect to man. Her fixed hypnotic gaze, as she slowly turns her head, follows your every movement. She is one of the few insects able to turn her head, an ability that contributes much to her uncannily knowing look. The two great, dull-colored eyes seem to have no pupils, but down in their depths a small dark dot is dimly visible. Between them, in the forehead, are three well-developed ocelli; one wonders what she perceives with them and if they are functional eyes at all.

Few insects give so much evidence of possessing some power of thought. True, the ant lion automatically casts up his spray of sand to engulf the hapless ant dashing frantically around the walls of his funnel, and the spider at the center of her web rushes forth at the right moment to dispatch her entangled victim. These are simple responses to obvious stimuli. But put a large, lively spider into the jar with your mantis. The spider has been disturbed by your handling and runs around and around, sometimes passing close to the mantis but always going too fast for even her catlike pounce. At first she rears as if to grab it—her normal response to the sight of an insect in motion—but then she makes no further move. She only waits, as though contemptuously, until the spider has settled down to catch its breath. Then, with infinite stealth and deliberation, she sets herself in a favorable position—and snick!—quicker than the eye can follow, she snaps her trap on it.

And one can scarcely deny that she employs a measure of discrimination when she has captured a great digger wasp gliding to the ground with a fat cicada to place in its burrow. There in her trap the mantis has both the furious wasp and the cicada, paralyzed by the wasp's sting. She considers her catch, turning her head this way and that. Then she grasps the wasp firmly and proceeds to eat it, letting the doped cicada drop to the ground, where she will retrieve it once the wasp is consumed. She shows no hesitation, no uncertainty. To all appearances, she deliberates and reaches the right conclusion. But who can say where instinctive behavior ends and thought begins?

Then there is her reaction to toads. Books tell us that some tropical mantises devour small toads and even small birds.

The Chinese mantis in the eastern United States does not eat toads, but her reaction to them is interesting. The Brooklyn Entomological Society records that once an experimenter offered a very small toad to a very hungry mantis. She seized it but dropped it immediately, and nothing could induce her to touch it again. I had a very large *Paratenodera sinensis* which I kept under a bell jar one summer in New Jersey. I had at the same time a half-grown toad which I sometimes introduced under the jar when I had time to watch and remain ready to effect a rescue if necessary. At least once each evening, and often two or three times, the mantis would, after long deliberation, swoop down in front of the toad and rear up, with underwings fully displayed, in what Fabre calls her "spectral" attitude. But having gone that far, her appetite for toad seemed to fail, and she never actually touched him. Possibly the toad's nervous reaction to the shock of her swoop elicited some mantis-repellant effluvium imperceptible to our gross sense. At any rate, she always checked herself on the very point of grabbing him. In the course of the summer the toad became quite blasé about it all, and although unable to keep from wincing a trifle, he would then sit motionless with drooped lids and a look of "Oh yeah?" on his toadish features. It is impossible to know whether the mantis uses some obscure reasoning power or whether she is controlled entirely by instinct.

But whether motivated by instinct or by the rudiments of reason, the behavior of the full-grown female mantis shows more variation and originality than is observable in the behavior of many other insects. Each mantis has her own marked individuality. Some are nervous and high-strung, quick to strike at any sudden motion. Some are so deliberate that it is hard to believe that they do not exercise judgment and weigh a choice of courses. Some make most interesting pets, because they will drink milk or water from a small dish or teaspoon, take bits of raw meat from the fingers, or sit companionably on the worktable, staring curiously at fingers or pen as you write, quite as if they were trying to comprehend. Others are always "stand-offish"; they will have none of you or your offerings and will starve to death rather than try an unaccustomed food. Some, having seized a prey, seem to know that a bite in the cervical ganglion will end the victim's struggles, and they put this knowledge to good use; but others, no less powerful and active, never acquire this precision of technique but catch the prey as they can and hold fast with the serrated arm, so that the captive continues his struggles until he is almost consumed. Some make a practice of biting off the head first. Others always start the meal by pulling off a leg and holding it up in a gloating manner, gazing at it with the head turning this way and that before eating it, while some sybaritic mantises will accept neither legs nor wings, thorax nor head, but plunge the triangular beak into the abdomen and lick out all the soft inner parts. These fussy females often leave the victim's outer parts almost intact, so that only by turning the body on its back can you see that nothing is left but a hollow shell, complete with legs and wings. This type is the hardest to provide for. Apparently the abdominal contents are less sustaining than the more muscular portions, and so the insect gourmet drains grasshoppers, crickets, cicadas, and so forth so rapidly that it takes much hunting to provision her larder.

The differences in behavior are paralleled by differences in the externals of nest-building. No two "nests," or egg cases, are exactly alike. This variation results not from whimsy but largely from sheer chance. The shape and size of the twig chosen to support the egg case, interruptions during the long business of nest-making and egg-laying, and possibly even the presence or absence of a breeze at the crucial time may serve to cause slight irregularities in the outer shape of the nest. Certain nests are as fancifully draped and swathed as a Moslem's turban; others are so nearly flat on top and bottom and so short as to make you think that a pat on each of four sides would reshape them into cubes. Occasionally a very small egg case occurs among large ones; it is made by a female that has already produced one or even two larger nests with their complement of eggs.

During its creation and for a very short time thereafter, the nest is almost pure white, very light, and frothy; but it starts to harden and darken in a few moments and stands all winter as an inconspicuous, dirty, sand-colored lump, hard to notice among the weeds and twigs. The mantises seem to regard certain trees and shrubs as especially well-suited to nest-building. Sometimes you may search for hours on a hillside without finding more than one or two nests and then suddenly discover a sapling bearing as many as 30 cases. Is it favorable location that determines the choice, or is it some quality of sturdiness or durability in the chosen twig?

Much remains to be learned about the mantis. Her increasing numbers and the fascination of observing her ways should tempt someone, perhaps now a mere Cub Scout learning first lessons in wood-craft, to make a full-time study of this one insect that is entirely beneficial to man.

THE HONEYBEE'S CHARADE ✦ A
breath-taking discovery in animal communication
✦ BY N. J. BERRILL, OF MCGILL UNIVERSITY.

ANIMALS move and plants vegetate, oysters and tumbleweed notwithstanding. And movement, if it is not merely drifting with the currrents of air or water, demands sensitive recordings as well as an operative mechanism. Movement is useful primarily because it puts the animal in the right place at the right time. Of course, the animal may only need to *stay* in the right place, as a jellyfish needs to stay above the dark void of the oceanic abyss. More often, movement is essential because it enables the creature to pursue prey or to escape capture. Another end of movement is seen in the more selfless enterprise of migration, in which the bird places its eggs in such a location that the succeeding generation will be in the right place at the right time—in other words, where the young will have the proper food and temperature at that time of year.

But whatever the aim, movement requires an animal to respond to factors that define its position in relation to the world around it. Many lowly animals move only in close contact with the ground and maintain an intimate sensory and locomotory connection through immediate touch, but most of them have some sensitivity to light to help them orientate themselves. It is when an animal leaves the sea floor to swim in a vast world of three dimensions, or abandons a pedestrian life on land for the adventure of flight, that navigation by reference to cosmic forces and internal sensations becomes paramount. Then, for most creatures, it is the light of the sun by day and the gravitational pull of the earth by night as well as day that maintain them in their course. Even the jellyfish has its eyespots and weighted sacs, whereby in light or darkness it manages to keep near the surface of the sea.

To state it another way, animals navigate mainly by the light of a star and the pull of a planet, though quite differently from the aviator with his mechanical instruments and mathematical tables. When speed is attained, the friction and pressures of the medium through which an animal travels are generally also taken into account. Friction may be lessened by streamlining, and pressures are likewise reduced, but they are not eliminated. And pressures actually have their own value. An animal that is traveling at high speed and is twisting and turning needs to be constantly responsive to stresses inherent in its maneuvers. Clearly, the creature requires an apparatus that is sensitive to speed and sharpness of turn in order to achieve precise control. So we find numerous pressure organs over the face of a fish, lying in an intricate system of surface channels. They send to the brain an accurate reflection of the water stream flowing past the head.

In the air, the flight and navigating powers of bats and birds present both wonders and mysteries, but these warm-blooded creatures are at least large enough to accommodate organs of considerable complexity. It is when we come to the insects that we gasp in wonderment, for here we see equally exquisite mechanisms for flight and the control of flight compressed into almost unbelievably small space. We know most about certain flies, particularly *Muscina stabulans,* and the honeybee, for these are the insects that have been studied the most. And while it may take a somewhat detached point of view to see beauty in a buzzing fly, its speed, hairpin turns, and pin-point landings demonstrate the superb performance of an aerial gymnast.

Something of how a fly does it has been discovered recently by Dr. F. S. J. Hollick, who devised a wind tunnel and balance such as is used for the study of aircraft but on a scale adapted to the size of a fly. Air was blown in various ways past a captive fly, and its wingbeats and other movements were delicately recorded. One flight instrument uncovered was an airspeed indicator situated in the third joint of the antennae. As air pressure increases on the head of the insect, the antennae become more and more deflected at the third joint, and the strains so set up stimulate the tension-recording sense organ at the base. This in turn sets off the various reflex adjustments of posture appropriate to the speed in question. Just how important the speed indicator is and how it influences flight is hard to say. But it does suggest forcibly that the insect not only flies but feels itself in flight and that this is important to the flight operation.

Even more informative than the antennal airspeed indicator is the turn indicator. This pair of organs, long known but only recently understood, are called the halteres. Readers of *Natural History* Magazine were introduced to the operation of the halteres in an article by Dr. C. H. Curran, "How Flies Fly," in the February, 1948, issue and incorporated into his book *Insects in your Life*. This article was based on the first successful high-speed motion pictures showing the action of the halteres in a Drone Fly. The fly has a pair of these, one on each side, below and slightly to the rear of the wing bases, and their rapid vibration provides the fly with the equivalent of a gyroscopic indicator. If the flying insect goes off course or tends to go into a spin, strains are caused in the basal sense organs, and these strains set off stimuli that initiate reflex flight stability. Without this living gyroscope, the fly could not make its sharp turns and twists without going out of control. This use of the gyroscope principle by various kinds of flies seems to be unique in the animal kingdom.

So much for flight itself. When it comes to navigation it is the bee that holds the honors.

If you were told that a bee returning from a trip to get

honey or pollen could "remember" how far it had traveled, what direction it had taken to get home, how good the supply was, and in the dark of the hive could "tell" the other bees just where to go to get some more, would you believe it? This is the story that came out of Austria after World War I from Professor Karl von Frisch. It sounds like a tall story, so tall in fact that a scientist at the University of Cambridge found it impossible to believe and yet at the same time found it impossible to disbelieve a man of von Frisch's standing. So there was only one thing for him to do—go to Austria and see for himself. The result was that the truth of the story was confirmed, and by a man who had originally doubted it. Such is the way of science, and in consequence we now must completely revise our ideas of what goes on in some of the tiniest brains in the world.

If men, instead of bees, were doing these things, we would say that the finder remembers how far he has traveled and in what direction, and that he tells his companions about the distance and location of food on the return, by gestures or by speaking. But the finder returning to the hive, and to her aroused nestmates, is a bee. How these things are retained by the bee, and how they are transmitted to the other bees, remains an unsolved problem. Bees do not learn their "language" as man learns his; rather, without any special process of learning, they seem to be capable of their "dances" on the comb and of reacting to the dancing of hivemates. But although we do not know as yet how these results are achieved, the facts that follow have been demonstrated with clarity.

When a worker bee discovers a large source of food, she "informs" the other workers in some way through her dance on the comb. The bees that are closest follow her in the dance, become excited, and then fly out in search of the food. This has been known for a good many years. Then it was noticed that there are two kinds of dances, the round dance and the waggle dance. If the food is less than 100 yards away, the bee performs the round dance. Somehow the round dance serves as a kind of signal to other bees to go out and search for food having the scent that the dancer acquired from the flower.

When distances become greater, this sort of searching could be a great waste of time and effort, but fortunately for the hive, the bees are able to avoid this by other resources of communication. The finders then start their waggle dances. This is much more complicated than the round dance. The bee runs across the middle of the cone, waggling her abdomen from side to side at a constant rate. This is merely part of the

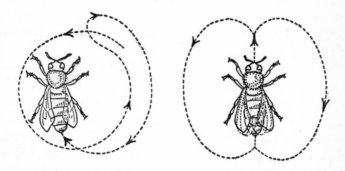

dance, and the whole dance is in the form of a figure eight, up the middle of the cone and down one side, up the middle and down the other side. The dance is repeated a number of times.

Now, what von Frisch and his skeptical visitor found was that by timing the dance with a stop watch, they themselves could tell roughly how far away the food supply was located, within 100 yards of being correct even when it was 5 miles away. If the food was between 100 and 200 yards from the hive, the dance was repeated about 10 times in 15 seconds. When it was 1000 meters away, the frequency of the dance dropped to four or five in every 15 seconds. This aspect of the dance has two very useful results for the hive. In the first place it excites the near-by bees, which follow behind it. And the frequency of the waltz in some way tells them how far they must fly to find the food. The teacher says in effect, "It is dark in here; stay close behind and do this after me!"

So much for the distance; what of the direction? Remember that the dance is performed in the dark on the vertical surface of a comb. The direction of the waggle-run across the center indicates the direction in which the food lies in relation to the position of the sun. If the waggle-run goes straight up the comb, the food is to be found by directly following the path toward the sun. If the run goes straight down the comb, it lies in the direction opposite to the sun. If the run goes to the right, the food is to be found to the right of the sun and at just such' an angle as the run makes with the vertical line of the comb. And the same relationship holds on the left.

The dance accordingly tells the following bees both the distance and the direction, and as soon as the other bees have gained the information, off they go. If there is still food when they get there, they gather it, return to the hive, and in their turn perform the waggle dance. And so more and more bees become excited and go harvesting. When finally the food is all gone, the returning workers dance no more, and the hive quiets down.

The more you think about all this, the more remarkable it becomes. It is almost like map making and map reading. For the bee does not point out the actual direction of the food, any more than a map actually points the way to New York. When the bee is moving straight up the cone, it means that the food supply lies in the direction of the sun, but it certainly does not mean that the sun or the food is overhead. So how is the information really conveyed? For when the dance is performed, it is in the darkness of the hive where the sun cannot be seen.

There are two forces that animals make use of to find their way in space. These are light and gravity. All animals that move rapidly through air or water know the pull of the earth and the light from the sun. And what the bee does when she waggles up the middle of the cone is to substitute gravity for light, to substitute the line to the center of the earth for the line to the sun. This is something like what you do when you draw a map. You draw an arrow which represents the direction of north, no matter how you turn the paper.

In some way the sense of gravity takes the place of light in whatever kind of mind the bee possesses, and the angle of the climb in relation to the straight pull downward of the force of gravity somehow is measured. Moreover, it is measured to an accuracy of about three degrees. As to how it is measured, we have as yet very little idea. In fact, one of the most puzzling things about the whole business is that the bee seems to have so little equipment with which to do it. The bee that has found the food takes measure in some way of the time or effort taken to get to it. Its senses record the direction of the flight home in relation to the position of the sun. It draws a map in the form of a dance, in which a line to the earth's center becomes a symbol for the line from the hive to the sun. And other bees following in the footsteps of the dance translate the movements and directions back from gravity to light and gain knowledge both of distance and direction. This is a far cry from our old idea of forced movements. We used to say that bees and other insects moved automatically and in a simple way in direct response to light or smell or some other stimulus, forced to move toward the light or away from it whether they wanted to or not.

The problem would be difficult enough if this were all. But it isn't. Outside the hive, the bees will give the distances and directions on a flat horizontal surface. The signaling bee then uses the actual line to the sun as the measuring line, and it uses the line of the waggle dance to point the real direction of the food. In complete darkness the bee can no longer do this, which is not surprising. What is surprising is that she can draw the sun line as long as a patch of sky can be seen, even if the sun is out of sight. And it has taken a very large number of experiments to discover more of what this means.

In the crucial experiments, von Frisch placed a "polaroid" screen over an opening in the top of a hive. As he rotated the screen into various positions, he saw that the dancing bees changed the line of their dance accordingly. This meant that they were sensitive to polarized light from the sky and could orientate themselves with regard to it, just as they could to the position of the sun itself. Now this complicates matters, for there is not much likelihood that the bees have any opportunity to perform the waggle dance horizontally within the hive. Yet the experiments do show a remarkable faculty for obtaining compass directions from polarized light, and the bees should have a use for it. And very recently the lowly ant has been shown to move in accordance with the direction of polarized light.

Natural polarized light outside is the light that passes from the sun and is reflected from the high sky at right angles to the sun down to the earth's surface. Such light rays are no longer scattered but are parallel, and if we could see them we would see a pattern of light in the sky, a pattern or zoning that the bees evidently do see. The bees are able to orientate themselves with relation to the sun even under a clouded sky so long as there is a patch of blue. When there is no blue, the bee must have unobstructed vision in the direction of the sun to detect its position. It is clear from von Frisch's experiments that bees depend greatly upon the polarized light of the sky for their orientation. But remember, the dance that follows does not give the angle of flight in relation to the polarized light; it still gives the flight angle relative to the position of the sun. The pattern of polarized light is used by the bee to locate the position of the sun, and the bearings are made in relation to that. And then, in the actual dance within the hive, it is translated on a vertical surface into a relationship with the plumb line of gravity.

Such is the way of science. We remove the veil in front of one mystery only to find a greater mystery lies behind.

❦ THE LASSOING SPIDER *❦* *The Bolas Spider spins her own "rope" and throws it with a cowgirl's skill* *❦* BY WILLIS J. GERTSCH, CURATOR, DEPARTMENT OF INSECTS AND SPIDERS, AMERICAN MUSEUM OF NATURAL HISTORY.

IN ALL societies, you are apt to find some nonconformists who persist in a determination not to follow the communal line of least resistance. Usually such heresy is productive of nothing that can survive, but also from such heretics may come the geniuses who originate new methods and establish new lines. Among the orbweaver spiders, we find a group that has broken so completely with the past that its members do not spin orb-webs at all but have substituted an entirely different method of capturing insects. Instead of relying on the static but dependable round web, they spin a line, weight it with a sticky drop of liquid silk, and hurl it at their prey, much as the gaucho throws his bolas or the angler casts his line.

No pounding hoofs or shrill cries attend the throwing of the viscid ball by *Mastophora,* the Bolas Spider, whose successful effort is marked at most by a frenzied beating of soft wings. Very quickly the fluttering ceases, and no record of the means of capture is evident when we see the spider with her bulky prey. Long before the South American Indian learned to throw his bolas of round stones tied to ropes of braided rawhide, the Bolas Spider was an accomplished boleadora. But she has kept her secret so well that few Americans know of her existence. With the license of an inventor, she keeps her line attached to the single bola and hurls it as a sort of lasso. The viscid ball is the noose that holds the unwilling prey until she enswathes it in bonds of silk.

Spiders have devised many ingenious methods for stopping and ensnaring flying insects. Most of these are based on a copious production of silk and the use of this strong, elastic material for expansive webs. Perhaps the one best known and most pleasing to the eye is the round web or orbweb, composed mostly of radiating and spiral threads. *Mastophora* belies her true heritage as an orbweaver and gains a livelihood by a parsimonious use of silk.

Such amazing creatures must come from far-off places, perhaps from the depths of tropical jungles or from little-known areas where few men live. Not so! These exotic spiders are found over most of the United States and are within reach of anyone with the inclination to find them and the time to observe their activities. Indeed, some of them seem to prefer the formal vegetation of our city parks and live in the shrubs and trees along the walks and riding lanes. Close relatives of the Bolas Spiders live in Australia, where their incredible habit of angling for prey has gained them the name of Angler Spiders. One of these heretics from Africa, *Cladomelea*, varies the fishing procedure by spinning its line around like a whirligig.

All are fat spiders of above average size, whose bodies are ornamented in a most grotesque manner. The carapace is bedecked with sharp, branched crests or horns and set with many small, rounded projections, whereas the voluminous abdomen is lined and wrinkled and surmounted with rounded humps. These bizarre specializations, reminiscent of such ornamention in the dinosaurs and many other groups of animals, are not known to play an important part in the life of the spiders. Indeed, there is little indication from the general appearance of these creatures that they do anything exciting. The spinelessness of the first pair of legs, and their greater length as compared with the other pairs, probably contribute to a better handling of the pendulum fishing line and thus may be said to be specialized for that purpose.

Fall is the best time to search for the Bolas Spiders, which, though not uncommon throughout their range, rarely come to our notice. Their failure to spin an expansive web, as do most of their relatives, increases the difficulty of discovering them. One factor that also contributes to their apparent rareness is their habit of living in bushes and trees, often at considerable heights. Usually we are attracted first to the conspicuous egg sacs and see near them one of these curious spiders. Once we have her, we can carry her home and install her in a convenient spot; or, better still, watch her in her own hunting grounds.

The site is usually an outer branch several feet above the ground in plain sight, and the spider may be exposed or only partially hidden from view during the day. Mementos of her previous activities are numerous silken lines, which soon form a thin coating over the twig and the leaves. Hanging to the lines or hidden among the near-by leaves may be one or more egg sacs, beautifully and durably made, and representing many hours of tireless spinning.

During the daylight hours, *Mastophora* clings to the twig or leaf, completely immobile, perhaps deriving some sort of protection from this simulation of an inanimate object. A confirmed introvert, she can be said to resemble a bud, a nut, a snail, or, with considerable faithfulness, a bit of bird dung. Indeed, her resemblance to bird lime makes one of her common names, the bird-dropping spider, quite appropriate. If we take her in our fingers, she shows only a momentary evidence of life and then quickly resumes her inanimate role. We roll her around in our cupped hands like a nut or marble, and she does not even respond when we accidentally drop her to the ground. Finally, we place her back on her perch and find, an hour or more later, that she has seemingly not moved an inch during our absence. Few spiders are so completely inscrutable.

But *Mastophora* is a creature of evening and night, and as we watch her later in the performance of her marvelous routine, we forgive the early listlessness she showed. The disappearance of the last rays of twilight is her signal for action, for soon after that she takes up her position for the evening's sport.

With her plump body swinging from the ends of numerous legs, she moves to one end of the branch and affixes her thread to the lower side by pressing her spinnerets against the bark. Grasping this thread with one of her hind legs and holding it away from the branch, she crawls along for several inches and finally pastes the line firmly at the other end. The result is a loosely hung line. She often moves about on it and strengthens it with an additional dragline thread. This strong trapeze line is strung far enough below the branch to allow a clear space for her fishing.

Moving to the center of the trapeze line, *Mastophora* now touches her spinnerets and pulls out a new thread, which lies clear of the other and is drawn out to a length of about two inches. Still keeping it attached to her spinnerets and held taut, she now combs out on the line quantities of viscid silk by means of her hind legs. Each leg alternates in combing out the liquid until a shining globule as large as a seed pearl is formed.

The spider now pulls out a greater length of line, allowing the weighted portion to drop part of the distance to its natural point of equilibrium, and then turns and severs the line just below the globule with the claws of one of her hind legs. The freed line swings back and forth like a pendulum, but the spider turns quickly and approaches it, searching and groping with a front leg until she is able to grasp it. Quickly she swings her massive body and grasps the trapeze line by the hind legs of one side and adjusts the fishing line between her palpi and one of her long front legs. Poised and ready now is the boleadora, and she waits for the approach of any suitable victim, with the patience that characterizes this spider.

Also roused to activity at this time of night are many nocturnal insects, which soon fly along their accustomed lanes, dipping down close to the foliage and fluttering in and out among the branches. A large-bodied moth, with wings spreading nearly two inches and with great eyes shining red in the last rays of reflected light, dips down toward the hunting grounds of the waiting spider. As the insect approaches, *Mastophora* gives every evidence of knowing of the nearness of a prospective victim. She moves her body and adjusts her line as if in tense expectancy. At just the right moment, when the moth comes within the reach of the line, the spider swings it rapidly forward in the direction of the flyer. The viscid ball strikes on the underside of a forewing and brings the winged creature to an abrupt stop, its tether an unyielding line that will stretch half its length before it will part.

Fluttering furiously at the end of the lasso, the moth makes every effort to free itself from the sticky globule, but the spider is quickly on hand to deal out the final coup by biting the victim on some part of its body. Resistance ends quickly with the venomous bite, and the paralyzed moth is rotated and trussed up like a mummy with sheets of silk. To the victor belong the spoils, and *Mastophora* now sets to work feeding on the body juices of her catch. This bountiful food supply will keep the spider busy for some time. After having satiated her appetite, she cuts loose the shrunken remnant from the trapeze line and drops it to the ground below. Later in the night a second capture may be made, but *Mastophora's* needs for food are usually well met by a single sizable victim.

It must not be concluded that the life of this spider is quite as simple as the incident portrayed might indicate. *Mastophora* may wait in vain for a flying creature to come near enough for capture. In many instances, her aim may not be as accurate as pictured, or the prospective victim may be too large to be held even by the strong band of silk. But patience is one thing at which spiders excel, and *Mastophora* is no exception. Should no victim reward her after half an hour of sitting with her line ready for casting, she winds the globule and line into a ball and eats it. Quickly she spins another line, prepares another sticky bead, and resumes her vigil.

How wonderfully complex is the pattern of instinctive activities that makes up the fishing habit of *Mastophora!* Although endowed with glands that produce silk in copious quantities, the spider now bases her whole economy on a blob of sticky silk dangling at the end of a short line. And still not content with a niggardly use of this vital material, she eats the viscid globule if it is not put to use against her prey. One would like to think that the stickiness of the viscid globule is impaired by exposure to the air, and that a wise spider is renewing it, but we know this is not the case. This action is often seen with great surprise by casual observers, but it is characteristic of the orb-weavers as a group. Perhaps it is inspired by the fact that they must so often roll up the lines of their tattered webs and build them up again.

Mastophora's lifeline is a silken dragline thread of great elasticity and of a tensile strength said to be second only to fused quartz fibers. The trapeze line, the pendulum thread, the viscid globule, and the instincts of the hungry spider combine to give us one of the most sensational of all devices for the capture of prey.

In September, 1903, there appeared in the *Scientific American* an article entitled "A Bolas-Throwing Spider," in which were given full details of the angling habit as practiced by *Mastophora cornigera*, one of the Bolas Spiders. We owe the first description of this moving drama to the patience and keen observation of Mr. Charles E. Hutchinson of Glendale, California. Nearly twenty years later, in 1922, the similar habits of the Australian Angler Spider, *Dicrostichus magnificus*, were described by Mr. Heber A. Longman, who knew nothing of Hutchinson's early paper. American spider specialists have likewise either forgotten or were completely unaware of the existence of this fine description of one of our most interesting spiders.

The Australian spiders of this group have been studied rather carefully by various workers, but the fundamental investigations are to be credited to Mr. Heber A. Longman of Brisbane. He noted the complete absence of a web of viscid silk and watched the remarkable method by which the Magnificent Angler Spider, *Dicrostichus magnificus,* caught one of the common Noctuid moths. His description deviates little from what we know of *Mastophora.* "From its slender bridge it would spin a filament, usually about one and a half inches in length, which was suspended downwards; on the end of this was a globule of very viscid matter, a little larger than the head of an ordinary pin, occasionally with several smaller globules above. This filament was held out by one of the front legs, the miniature apparatus bearing a quaint resemblance to a fisherman's rod and line. On the approach of a moth, the spider whirls the filament and globule with surprising speed, and this is undoubtedly the way in which it secures its prey. The moths are unquestionably attracted to an effective extent by the spider, whether by scent or by its color we cannot say. We certainly could not distinguish the slightest odor. But the fact remains that night after night one or two moths would flutter up and be caught. Other moths near by seemed to be indifferent, but two were often secured in the space of an hour, one of which would be packed away on the line to be sucked later. The spectacle of the moth fluttering up to the spider, sometimes two or even three times before it was caught, is one of the most interesting little processes which the writer has ever witnessed in natural history. The supposed desire of the moth for the star is a poet's fancy, but the attraction of the moth to the *Dicrostichus,* although mysterious, can be seen by any patient watcher."

We have saved mention of the *Cladomelea* from Africa until the end of this section, because the habits of this species are a further innovation. *Cladomelea* spins the same horizontal threads as do the other species and attaches the usual perpen-

dicular line with a viscid globule at its end. Instead of holding
the weighted line with the long front legs as do her cousins,
Cladomelea grasps it by the third or shortest leg and uses her
other legs to secure herself to the trapeze lines. Mr. Conrad
Akerman of Pietermaritzburg, South Africa, tells us that "This
spider does not wait for the appearance of her prey and then
hurl the droplet at it as with *Dicrostichus magnificus,* but
whirls it rapidly on the end of its thread with a rotary motion
in a horizontal plane. She keeps up this movement for about
fifteen minutes without a pause, then draws up the thread and
swallows the viscid droplet. After resting a few minutes she
repeats the performance, spinning another line with a terminal
globule and rotating it again for about fifteen minutes. Should
any insect come within the radius of the circling droplet it
would be struck with considerable force, and so, I imagine,
would be captured by sticking to the viscid matter; the spider
could then seize it or enshroud it in silk. The droplet is always
rotated in a clear place and never struck any of the stationary
objects in its vicinity."

Thus we note that already *Cladomelea* has introduced a
refinement to the fishing line in the design of a whirligig. Or
perhaps the converse is true—the measured, less wasteful practice of *Mastophora* may represent the real advancement in
technique.

The habit of angling for prey must be a very old one, inasmuch as it is shared by spiders in such widely separated areas
as Africa, Australia, and America. Just when it arose and what
inspired it belong at present only within the realm of speculation; the solution must await fuller data on this group and on
related spiders. The place of origin of this new method is tied
up with the origin of the group itself, and of that we know
nothing. Nor are enough of the spiders known to give us some
clue, in their structure or in the instincts of the young, to the
probable beginnings of the group.

We are inclined to be dogmatic in our belief that these

spiders were once nearly typical orbweavers, but just how long ago this was we can only surmise. It seems reasonable to suppose that the angling habit arose within the web itself and that the orbweb was discarded only after the habit was perfected. The repudiation of the orbweb must have occurred some time after the new process was devised, for dependence on the orb must have been fairly complete at the time the new habit was forming. We can visualize the parent spider of the group on her orb in the process of subduing a fluttering insect and see her force out great sheets or drops of viscid silk to entangle it. We have only to place one of these globules on the end of a short line to have the fishing line of *Mastophora*. The instinctive actions that gradually refined the technique and guided the spider to the normal position for holding the line must have been acquired very slowly, perhaps only after long periods of time. Once the new method proved a success, the orbweb became superfluous and was finally lost altogether in its normal form. Perhaps in the trapeze lines of the Bolas Spider we have a vestige of the once mighty orbweb.

In a recent letter, Mr. Hutchinson informed me that the angling habit is fully developed in young females one-fourth grown. However, the activities of young spiderlings just beginning to capture their prey still remain a mystery. We know that young spiderlings have little need for food soon after emerging, but efforts to maintain and study them have so far been unsuccessful. Perhaps in the early habits of some of the other species or some other orbweaver heretic we may discover a hint or definite recapitulation of the ancient practices of these atypical round-web spinners.

In all of the descriptions of the angling habit there have been speculations as to the role of the moth in the drama. Some principle of attraction seems to impel the victim to fly toward the spider, indeed to return repeatedly if it does not become entangled the first time. Hutchinson, who studied *Mastophora* very thoroughly and has continued his interest in the spider to the present time, found the method of capture a most successful one and was inclined to believe that an agreeable odor was emitted either by the spider or the silken line. The dearth of suitable moth prey in the vicinity and the consistent success of the spider contributed to this inference. Longman's conclusions were similar, and they are largely contained in our quotation from his splendid paper. It seems reasonable to suppose that the attraction must be the chemical one of odor or a visual one. The moth is probably well supplied with receptors for space perception, for we know that many moths are attracted to baits and other odoriferous objects.

On the other hand, it is more probable that visual stimuli could be responsible for sending the moth into the jaws of the spider. The compound eye of the moth is a wonderful organ, specialized for nocturnal use and no doubt responsive to even small quantities of light stimulus. The glistening globule of viscid silk or, perhaps, the pale body of the spider itself, might be sufficiently illuminated by light rays, either not evident to man's diurnal eye or outside his visual range, to cross the responsive threshold in the eye of the moth.

However, there is no real evidence that either of the above alternatives even approximates the truth. The true explanation may well be that the whole business is only a fortuitous one, largely dependent on the random flying activities of the moth. Mere chance would bring one or more within the reach of the spider almost every night, and if not, the creature could go without food for days or weeks without being profoundly affected. Although this solution would be at variance with the reasonable impressions of two eminent investigators, its simplicity has much in its favor.

But let us return to *Mastophora*, who hangs on her trapeze line and awaits the approach of her prey. With what senses does she detect the presence of the flying insect and know just when to hurl the viscid globule? Her eight small eyes are of little use to her, and at night they probably convey no visual impressions at all. At the expense of better eyesight, her progenitors developed an expansive web and substituted touch-vision to keep them informed of activity in any part of it. Her relatives respond to the presence of prey by rushing to the spot and are informed of its nature by the vibratory disturbance. Although reduced in size, the web on which *Mastophora* hangs in mid-air is still adequate as a sounding board. She feels the vibrations heralding the arrival of the moth and orients herself accordingly.

The egg sacs of the Bolas Spiders are hardly less spectacular than the spiders themselves. As is the case with many spiders, the process of laying the eggs and encasing them in a distinctive sac is a long and exhausting ritual. Even so, several egg sacs may be spun by the same female at intervals of about a week apart. In *Mastophora* the sacs are essentially equal in size to the spider herself and are hung near the site of the angling grounds, sometimes in the sun but more often partly protected by leaves. The sacs are hard objects that resemble nuts or other plant fruits. The distinctive feature of the sacs is the long stem, which is drawn off the rounded base and attached to twigs or leaves, and the globular base, which is variegated with light and dark kinds of silk. In one of our species the base is broadly attached to a twig, and the stem is free. In another the sac is somewhat bell-shaped and embellished with lateral extensions, the whole resembling a small, dried apple.

The female usually dies in the late fall and rarely lives to see her progeny emerge from the egg sac, an event that ordinarily occurs in the spring. The emergence of the spiderlings from the cocoon is an occasion of great moment in the life of the species and a thrilling sight to one who is lucky enough to be on hand to watch it. A small opening near the base of the stem, perhaps the result of concerted action on the part of the creatures inside, is barely large enough to allow each tiny spiderling to wriggle through. As soon as one has emerged, another appears at the small opening, and then another, until they are out in considerable numbers and beginning to string their silken lines on neighboring objects. The instinct to move upward asserts itself strongly, and soon many of the spiderlings are scattered far from the egg sac and many of them are being wafted into the air on their silken lines. Within a few hours, the whole family of perhaps 150 spiderlings may be far dispersed from the site of the empty egg sac. Inasmuch as some female bolas spin as many as five egg sacs, the possible progeny from a single spider may be as many as 700 spiderlings. The rarity of adult spiders of this group indicates that the mortality must be exceedingly high among their newly emerged spiderlings.

Up to now, all of our attention has been focused upon the female Bolas Spider and her egg sacs. What about her mate? The answer is found in a closer perusal of the spiderlings wriggling out of the small aperture in the cocoon before us. Some of the creatures are much redder than the others and have the tiny palpi armed with bulbous enlargements, which signalize the male spider. Closer inspection shows that these palpi are fully developed and indicates that these pygmies, averaging about one-sixteenth inch in length, are the mates of the Bolas Spider, which herself frequently attains a body length ten times as great. These adult males crawl out of the sac in company with baby sisters of equal size, which will not become full-grown and sexually mature for several months.

After studying the contents of various egg sacs in different stages of development, we are able to reconstruct the probable happenings within the egg sac. Several days or weeks after the eggs are laid, their pearly white shells break and allow the still embryonic spiders greater freedom for further development. The first true molt brings to light the creature we know so well as a spiderling, a small replica of the adult, which is able to spin and to eat. The males at this stage are precocious and have the palpi enlarged, but they are still not fully developed, being comparable in appearance to the penultimate stage of most male spiders. Following the first true molt, most spiders break out of the egg sac, and no doubt that happens often with *Mastophora.* However, very frequently another molt is undergone within the egg sac before the males walk out of the sac—perfect adults as far as we are able to judge on the basis of external appearance. Naturally, we have no way of knowing without resorting to histological means whether a corresponding maturity is present within the creature, but from analogy with most other spiders, we can predict that this is probably so.

From an egg sac of *Mastophora cornigera,* sent to me from California through the generosity of Mr. Hutchinson, there issued on September 1, 147 spiderlings, of which 72 were baby females and 75 mature males. The young sisters that desert the egg sac in company with their tiny brothers must undergo several molts before they attain maturity. The question that immediately arises is whether there are in the vicinity contemporary, mature females to be matched with the precocious males. If emergence occurs in the fall, which in California may be a more frequent occurrence than is generally supposed, many females may still be available, and perhaps even the parent female may be visited by one of her precocious sons. On the other hand, it is probable that the new generation emerges oftener in the spring, and that the tiny males must then live through the long months until the female spiderlings attain adulthood.

Rarely within the limits of one small group of creatures do we find such an array of startling peculiarities and amazing habits. Such sensational performers deserve fuller study from biologists lucky enough to come in contact with them.

THE GLOWWORM GROTTO *New Zealand's beautiful but deadly fly larvae of Waitomo Cave* BY ALTON L. BLAKESLEE.

HOMEWARD bound from the 1946-47 Navy South Polar Expedition, the U.S.S. "Mount Olympus" rode the gray Pacific under a slaty sky, just out of Wellington, New Zealand.

In a stateroom, a scientist shook his head in a gesture of disbelief. "That," he said, "was simply magnificent."

He was thinking back not to Antarctica—the austere beauty of ice in mammoth cliffsides or delicate little castles, or the grandeur of icebergs or of glaciers spilling between mountains—but to a cave in New Zealand. For this is a cave with a brilliant underground sky of hundreds of thousands of living "stars," a cavern hung with silvery necklaces and echoing to the plinking music of dripping water. It's a scene of eerie beauty but all of it designed for tortuous, silent death so that some little worms may live.

During a week in New Zealand, more than a dozen of us from the expedition flagship—Navy officers, civilian scientists, and newsmen—visited this cave. Our careers, collectively, had taken us to many parts of the world, and we had witnessed many natural wonders in dozens of countries. But none of us could recall anything possessing the same breath-taking impact of sheer loveliness as the glowworm grottoes of the Waitomo Caves, 200 miles north of Wellington.

The Waitomo Caves are like numerous limestone caverns elsewhere—moist, chill, huge, and winding, with slow drops of water patiently building grotesque statues and pillars and columns of stalagmites and stalactites. Dutifully behind a guide whose voice boomed in rolling echoes, we toured the caves one night.

145

"Now, gentlemen, please be quiet. We're coming to the glowworms. If you make noise, they'll turn out their lights."

A Navy doctor laughed. For weeks on our voyage there had been a standing joke about "ice-worms" supposedly found in the ice at Little America and tasting—so one veteran of a previous expedition maintained—like spaghetti. Glowworms rigged with push-button lights that switched off at the sound of human voices were a phenomenon in the same category . . .

From the dim recesses of one long cavern hall, we followed the guide, one by one, into a completely dark passageway and then stood thunderstruck. On the vaulted ceiling of this cave shone a carpet of blue-green stars, round and unblinking, massed thick as daisies in a field.

From the thousands of lights, each half the size of a dime, came a glow that slowly, as our eyes adjusted, etched the walls of this cave. The walls were torn and rugged, as by once-rushing waters. Beneath flowed a dark river, reflecting back each little pin point of starlight in this buried heaven of the glowworm.

Suddenly the guide flicked the beam of a flashlight upward. The bright star-studded sky disappeared. Instead, we saw the cavern roof, creamy white and jagged and coated with small glistening sacs. From the roof streamed myriads of straight, gleaming, silky threads, a foot to two feet long. Each was gossamery as a spider's thread, but thicker, and strung every inch or so with a beadlike thread of mucus stuff.

Along the surface of the placid river there swarmed clouds of gnats, midges, and flies, coming upward to the "stars." Now one of the hanging threads vibrated. A gnat had brushed against it, sticking to it like an insect on flypaper suspended from the ceiling of an old farm kitchen. The guide snapped off his flashlight.

Then he began explaining. And as he did, in the cavern, dark save for the gleaming stars, the lights nearest to us flickered out. The glowworms were reacting to sound, as he had warned.

For all these stars are simply worms. They are the glowworm larvae, one stage in the fantastic life cycle of a strange fly (*Arachnocampa luminosa*) native only to New Zealand. It exists nowhere else.

In the beginning, the fly lays its eggs upon the ceiling of a moist cave, over a slow-moving river. The eggs are fastened to the roof by a mucus glue. The egg hatches into a larva, or worm, less than an inch long and with a transparent skin that makes all its internal organs visible. This grub is dirty gray in color, slimy, fragile, and legless; it has a segmented body, and it carries its own lamp. In its tail segment, by chemical action, it produces cold light like that of the firefly but a lighter blue in color. It can keep this lamp lighted continuously or can dim or extinguish it.

The luminous worm shelters itself within a silken sheath attached horizontally to the cavern wall and saturated with a slimy fluid. This sheath is about two inches long, and the grub can undulate back and forth inside it. From the sheath it suspends silken threads of mucus material exuded from its mouth. The threads, interspersed every few inches with a mucus globule and gleaming in the light like a diamond necklace, range from half a dozen inches to as much as two feet long, and one worm may spin fifteen to twenty of them.

The threads are death snares for flies and midges living on the waters beneath. Attracted by the synthetic starlight, the midge becomes caught on the sticky thread and struggles violently to escape—but in vain. The glowworm reswallows the thread like an angler reeling in his line and devours its victim whole.

These beaded pendulums also serve as the glowworm's ears, transmitting the vibrations of sound and warning the worm of possible dangers.

The meat-eating or carnivorous stage of the larva lasts for

several months. Then the glowworm reabsorbs all of its threads and changes into a chrysalis, hanging down on one single thread from its silken sheath. During this time, it remains luminous but does not eat. A few days later, the adult insect, the fly, emerges. This fly is about twice the size of a mosquito—a dainty creature with dark wings. Little is known of the insect during this stage of its life cycle, for the adult fly shuns daylight and seldom is seen, our guide explained.

But later, when the adult circles up to the cavern ceiling to lay its eggs, it brushes past the hanging threads without becoming caught. It is an example of Nature's perfect planning —the young cannot devour their elders returning to start the life cycle anew.

Only in the Waitomo Caves have the glowworms been found in such numbers. In lesser profusion, they are known elsewhere in New Zealand but in no other country. Some are found in the Botanical Garden in Wellington, in moist pathways or in cuttings above river banks, but only in handfuls at a time. Drying winds and the sun shrivel their threads, which usually are shorter in length in these locations. But the moist, dark caves are a perfect environment both for the glowworms and for the midges, which hatch from eggs laid in the muddy river bank and provide an abundant food supply for the worms. Were the caves larger, the number of glowworms might well run into millions.

This one resplendent cavern was small, but our guide led us downward deeper into the caves to a small pier jutting out into the silent river. Cautiously we stepped into a large rowboat, and wordlessly the guide, pulling hand over hand on wires strung at shoulder height, drew the boat over the cool waters flowing gently over the muddy bottom.

Here the stars shone in such profusion—by the hundreds of thousands—as to make the Milky Way blush with shame at its own poor brilliance. From this tremendous underground galaxy—where sometimes neighboring stars etched the familiar patterns of well-known constellations—there came a soft suffusive glow that was bright enough to outline the grotesque forms of hanging fingers, the statues and castle spires of the limestone formations. Palely the light shone back from the river surface, and here the reflected stars danced from the ripples fanning outward from the gliding boat.

Rarely there comes a shooting star, a meteor streaking down out of this buried sky, when one of the glowworms for some reason falls. In this shadowy midnight darkness, a few shone now on the muddy river bank, glowing for a while like tiny lighthouses set in the midst of the blackened ocean.

Everywhere there was music, as water from the ceiling plinked in uneven cadence upon the river, producing sounds silvery or deep in tone as the drops struck from greater or lesser heights. It was as though death strummed some inviting guitar.

For long awe-struck minutes we glided over the river, then wheeled in a wide circle, and suddenly these artificial stars paled in brilliance. Momentarily we were puzzled. It was not only that the stars were less richly massed; they also seemed dimmer. And then we realized—at this point the cavern wall opened upon the real night sky of the heavens. We were looking at Nature's own sky of real burning stars, devoid of moon at the moment, and we found it small, sparse, and dim compared with the galaxy fashioned by delicate, ethereal worms, the stars of death.

❧ THE ARCHER FISH ❧ *It shoots insects with a pellet of water—or douses cigarettes* ❧ BY HUGH M. SMITH, FORMERLY FISHERIES ADVISOR TO THE KINGDOM OF SIAM.

WHEN I went to Siam to study the remarkable fish life of the fresh and salt waters, one of the things I was most anxious to do was to make the intimate acquaintance of the archer fish, a creature that gets its living by a unique practice which had never been satisfactorily explained by scientists.

In the eighteenth century and earlier, vague accounts reached Europe regarding an oriental fish that obtained its food, consisting of insects, by knocking them down with drops of water propelled from its mouth. These accounts, unsupported by reliable evidence, doubtless met with a mixed reception on the part of zoologists and the general public; and it may be imagined that the scientific world of that day was eager to obtain authentic information concerning a creature whose behavior was so different from that of any other known fish.

The first definite printed reference to the fish in a European language seems to have been published in the year 1765, in the *Philosophical Transactions of the Royal Society of London.* At a meeting of the society held on March 15, 1764, a communication[1] was read from John Albert Schlosser, M.D., F.R.S., of Amsterdam, announcing the presentation to the society of a specimen of the fish which, to quote him, "I believe hath never been observed by any writer on natural history." The communication carried a description of the peculiar habits of the fish on the authority of a Mr. Hommel, governor of a hospital

[1] "An Account of a Fish from Batavia, called Jaculator." *Philosophical Transactions,* Vol. LV, for the year 1764, pp. 89-91, plate 9.

in Batavia, who was also the collector of the specimen. Designated as "the jaculator or shooting fish, a name alluding to its nature," the creature was described as follows:

It frequents the shores and sides of the sea and rivers, in search of food. When it spies a fly sitting on the plants, that grow in shallow water, it swims on to the distance of four, five or six feet, and then, with surprising dexterity, it ejects out of its tubular mouth a single drop of water, which never fails striking the fly into the sea, where it soon becomes its prey. The relation of this uncommon action of this cunning fish raised the governor's curiosity; though it came well attested, yet he was determined, if possible, to be convinced of the truth, by ocular demonstration. For that purpose, he ordered a large, wide tun to be filled with seawater; then had some of these caught, and put into it, which was changed every other day. In a while, they seemed reconciled to their confinement; then he determined to try the experiment. A slender stick, with a fly pinned on at its end, was placed in such a direction, on the side of the vessel, as the fish could strike it. It was with inexpressible delight, that he daily saw these fish exercising their skill in shooting at the fly with amazing dexterity, and never missed the mark.[2]

A second article on this fish,[3] also contributed by Doctor Schlosser, contained a description of the fish in Mr. Hommel's

[2] Unfortunately for the accuracy of the record, the fish to which Hommel referred and the specimen he sent to London were entirely different species. Appended to the article was a copy of a dscription given in 1754 by Linnaeus of a species called *Chaetodon rostratum* (known in later years as *Chelmo rostratus*), and the accompanying plate was of that fish of the coral reefs. There was thus precipitated the misunderstanding and doubt concerning this fish which lasted for nearly a century and a half.

[3] "Some further Intelligence relating to the Jaculator Fish." *Transactions of the Philosophical Society,* Vol. LVI, for the year 1766, pp. 186-188, plate 8, fig. 6. Doctor Schlosser this time presented another specimen. A description of it under the name *Sciaena jaculatrix* was given by the German zoologist Pallas. A poor but easily recognizable illustration accompanied the article. The allocation of the species with the sciaenid fishes, or drums, was unfortunate, as there is not even a remote relationship; and in 1817 Cuvier corrected the error and established the genus Toxotes for the reception of the fish which has since been known as *Toxotes jaculator.* This form and five closely related species constitute the family Toxotidae, peculiar to the oriental region.

own words and gave additional information on the fish's peculiar habits.

During practically the whole of the nineteenth century there seem to have been no new observations on the shooting powers attributed to the archer fish and no confirmation of the statements made by Hommel in 1765 and 1767. On the contrary, the leading authorities on oriental fishes denied that the fish did or could perform as claimed.

Dr. Pieter Bleeker, "the most active ichthyologist that ever lived," who spent more than 35 years studying the fishes of the orient, was the author of more than 400 articles on those fishes. He was also long a resident of the same city (Batavia) as Hommel, but he was unable to verify the early accounts of the jaculator fish and in 1875 expressed the belief that it did not deserve the celebrity that had been imposed on it. He believed that its reputation was based on an error of observation.

Dr. Francis Day, who devoted more than a quarter of a century to the investigation of the fishes of India and Burma and published monumental works thereon, withheld from Toxotes any credit whatever for its extraordinary shooting ability and erroneously ascribed to the coral-reef fish Chelmo the same ability. Thus, in "The Fauna of British India—Fishes" (1889), Day disposed of Toxotes in these words:

It is stated in some works that these wide-mouthed fishes shoot insects with a drop of water in Batavia. Bleeker observed that he never witnessed this, and the action is one which the mouths of these fishes appear incapable of effecting.

In an earlier article,[4] "On Asiatic Blowpipe Fishes," Day argued that Hommel's account could not have applied to Toxotes and could only have referred to Chelmo. He claimed that "no one, that I can ascertain, has asserted that *Toxotes jaculator,* with its deeply cleft mouth, was able to use it as a blow-

⁴ *Zoölogist,* 1881, p. 91.

pipe," and said further that "personally I paid special attention
to this question when investigating the fishes of Burma, but
no fisherman had ever heard of this ingenuity being attributed
to Toxotes, and which I cannot help thinking, with the late
Doctor Bleeker, must be an error."

The original misunderstanding and the perpetuation of the
error by Bleeker, Day, and others can undoubtedly be explained in some measure by the fact that among the Malays
both Toxotes and Chelmo are called by the same name, *sum-
pit-sumpit* (from *sumpitan*, a blowpipe).

One more quotation from a reputable source may be given
to illustrate the attitude of mind toward the most characteristic
habit attributed to the archer fish. This is from a notice of Toxotes by the late Professor J. S. Kingsley appearing in the *Standard Natural History* (Vol. 3, 1885):

> One of the species has been generally credited with the faculty
> of shooting drops of water at insects on low-hanging branches and
> thus securing them for food. There does not appear to be any
> adaptation in the organization of the mouth for such a feat, and
> skepticism must be exercised in the acceptance of the statement
> made. Certainly no recent confirmation of the old story has been
> given, and the tradition has probably resulted from some misunder-
> standing.

Although several minor notices of the habits of Toxotes
appeared in European periodicals in the last two or three years
of the nineteenth century, it was not until the dawn of the
twentieth century that this fish may be said to have finally
come into its own. The observations of a Russian ichthyologist,
Zolotnisky, definitely corroborated the essential facts of behavior as set forth in the earliest published accounts.[5] A number
of living specimens had been obtained in Singapore, and these

[5] Zolotnisky's detailed report, "Le Poisson Archer (*Toxotes jaculator*) en
Aquarium," was issued in 1902 in *Archives de Zoologie Experimentale et
Generale*. Vol. X, pp. lxxiv-lxxxiv.

were subjected to close scrutiny and experimentation, with the result that not only were the long-disputed habits fully established but new items of behavior were noted and set forth.

Among the facts regarding Toxotes that were recorded by Zolotnisky and have been confirmed by the present writer and other persons in Asia and America were the following:

(1) The fish subsists largely on insects that hover over the water or rest on overhanging vegetation. When a fish approaches within a certain distance of an insect, it becomes stationary, points its head and turns its eyes directly at the prey, brings the front of its mouth to the surface of the water, partly opens the mouth, and forthwith propels a drop, or several drops, of water at the insect, which ordinarily is 12 to 20 inches distant, but may be 40 inches or more. The aim is true, and the insect falls into the water and is at once devoured.

(2) The fish frequently swims backward. This habit is often observed when the fish reconnoiters a prospective prey and backs from it in order to secure a good position for observation and attack.

(3) The eyes sparkle with seeming intelligence, and their mobility is noteworthy. They can be directed sideways, upward, and backward but may not be turned downward.

(4) Aerial vision is acute. Even small insects may be seen at a great distance and fall a prey to the fish's amazingly accurate aim.

(5) Discrimination and selection are apparently exercised in the choice of food. Considerable ingenuity is sometimes employed in obtaining food; and in shooting at insects the distance and the force are gauged.

Zolotnisky's paper was made the basis for a critical review of "The Archer Fish and Its Feats" by the erudite Dr. Theodore Gill, published by the Smithsonian Institution in 1909;[6] and the foregoing statement of Zolotnisky's observations is largely a paraphrase of Gill's rendering. Gill found it difficult to accept

[6] *Smithsonian Miscellaneous Collections,* vol. 52, part 3, pp. 277-286.

some of Zolotnisky's statements and in concluding his paper said:

> This summary is a true version of the article by Zolotnisky and will doubtless excite skepticism among physiologists at large as well as psychologists. It contravenes certain assumptions respecting the power and range of vision among fishes, as well as of the intelligence and reasoning powers of such lowly animals. The extent of expression assigned to eyes destitute of mobile surroundings and accommodative adjustments may also be deemed to be exaggerated. Distinction therefore must be exercised between the facts observed (or alleged to have been observed) and the inferences respecting such facts. It must be conceded, however, that fishes which manifest such peculiar action as the archers should be subjects for still more elaborate observations and experiments.

In recent years in America many people have become acquainted with the archer fish and its performances through examples in aquaria in New York, Philadelphia, and other cities; and a motion picture of a fish in action has been made at the New York Aquarium. The present generation of fish students everywhere may be pardoned for expressing surprise at the protracted skepticism and wonder at the failure of doubting oriental ichthyologists to conduct practical tests.

One searches the literature in vain for an explanation or suggestion as to how an archer fish is able to propel a drop of water with such force and accuracy that it can dislodge insects on overhanging vegetation or hit them on the wing.

The doubt shown by zoologists of the last century in regard to the reputed shooting powers of the fish was partly due to their failure to detect in the fish's mouth any special mechanism by which drops of water could be formed and expelled.

It is, of course, obvious that there must be some peculiar adaptation or apparatus in Toxotes to account for its extraordinary accomplishment. Let this be the occasion to point out, for the first time, the special anatomical and physiological features on which the shooting performance depends.

By carefully watching the fish at close range on many occasions in Siam, I formed an opinion of the probable propelling mechanism, and I subsequently verified that opinion by holding the fish in a basin or bucket of water in the position regularly assumed when shooting and making it perform almost at will. This was accomplished by the quick, forceful compression of the gill covers with my fingers. I was able to cause a fairly satisfactory imitation of the normal shooting act and had no difficulty in propelling drops of water for distances up to three feet.

This compression of the gill covers would in itself not be adequate to account for the escape from the mouth of water in the form of individual drops of uniform size; and it is to the peculiar shape and structure of the mouth parts that we must look for the additional factors necessary for the complete and perfect performance.

The mouth cavity of Toxotes is long, but its diameter is much restricted by the projecting sides of the roof and by the large tongue. Indeed, when the tongue is raised, it may completely close the passage from the outer air to the pharynx. The forward part of the tongue is free from the floor of the mouth, and its rounded tip is of paper-like thinness and fits snugly against the palate. Behind, the tongue is thick, and it bears minute teeth and has a conspicuous fleshy prominence. Extending along the middle of the roof of the mouth, from a point just behind a band of vomerine teeth to the pharynx, are two low ridges, close together and parallel for most of their length but slightly diverging at the back. Between the ridges is a deep groove which, when the tongue is applied to the roof of the mouth, becomes converted into a tube. This groove-tube, which in a fish seven inches long is less than a sixteenth of an inch in diameter, has not been previously described or referred to in ichthyological writings, but it is readily seen when the tongue is depressed. That it should have been over-looked so long is something of a mystery when one recalls the vain efforts made by oriental ichthyologists to discover any special adaptation for drop-shooting.

We are now ready to appreciate how the shooting fish operates. With the tongue closely pressed against the palate, the sudden compression of the gill covers forces water from the pharynx into the palatine canal; and with the tip of the tongue acting as a valve, the flow of water under pressure is regulated. It is the obvious habit of the fish to co-ordinate the compression of the gill covers with the momentary lifting of the tongue from the front end of the tube, permitting the escape of a single drop of water. With the jaws partly separated and the mouth reaching or projecting slightly above the surface, the drop of water is ejected for a distance that depends on the pressure. It is easy to understand how, with the pharyngeal cavity serving as both a reservoir for water ammunition and a compression chamber, it is possible for the fish to shoot drops of water in quick succession, as has been frequently observed, or the water may be expelled in the form of a jet when the valve is kept open longer.

The drop-propelling function would be useless if Toxotes did not possess, in addition, the ability to use its eyes in the air and to gauge accurately the distance, size, and edibility of small creatures flying or resting near the water's edge. It is an outstanding point that, for a fish, the aerial vision of Toxotes is very keen; and it was always a surprise to me to note the readiness with which insects and spiders were sighted as the fish explored the vegetation on the bank of a pond or stream.

The extent to which the fish's head projects at the surface of the water during the shooting depends on circumstances. In muddy water, the eyes must be at the surface in order to permit a good view and accurate aim; in clear water, only the tip of the jaws need project.

This accomplishment of the archer fish has been developed and is exercised in order to obtain living food, consisting chiefly of insects. Enough has already been stated in regard to the general habit, but some definite references to food and feeding may be of interest.

This fish, with shapely, compressed body propelled by its broad caudal fin, is a graceful swimmer, moving quickly without apparent effort. It regularly swims at or just below the surface and may go a long distance in a perfectly straight line, making a wake with the tip of its jaws. This wake is characteristic and enables an observer to detect the presence of a fish even before he has actually seen it.

The habit of swimming at the surface is ascribable to two circumstances. The food on which the fish chiefly subsists is obtainable there; and the eyes, on which the fish largely depends, could not otherwise function properly, for during most of the year the waters in which Toxotes lives are very muddy or turbid and aquatic vision is much restricted.

While Toxotes prefers the live food which it shoots for itself, it regularly eats shrimps, insect larvae, and other creatures living in the water and insects that have fallen into the water. A large nest of carpenter ants impaled on a stake in a pond provided food for fish for several days; as the ants fell into the water, they were eagerly devoured. Under both semi-domesticated and wild conditions, the fish does not reject bits of raw and cooked meat, fish, crabs, and prawns. Specimens of Toxotes that I had in a pond regularly came to be fed on raw chopped pork and fish.

In Siam, Toxotes is often sought by anglers, who use a light rod and line, armed with a small hook baited with a shrimp or insect. Favorite resorts for the fish—and hence for anglers—are the inlets and outlets of canals, near locks. A person in a small boat, casting his hook well away from the boat and doing nothing to frighten the fish, may often catch many at one place. The food value of the fish is high.

Once, in Bangkok, I saw a baby lizard, sunning itself on a vertical timber of a dock a few inches above the water, dislodged by a surprise shot of a Toxotes operating at point-blank range. As the lizard fell, it was promptly grasped, but there may be doubt as to whether it was actually consumed. The cavity of this fish's mouth is too narrow and the sides are too rigid to permit the passage of a large mass of food. It is apparent that seized insects and other food must first be reduced to a slender bolus between the tongue and the various bands of minute teeth on the roof of the mouth before swallowing is possible.

Some of the standard modern works of reference and textbooks make inadequate or misleading allusion to the exercise of the shooting power. Thus, when the *Cambridge Natural History* states that "*Toxotes jaculator* derives its name from its habit of capturing insects flying over the surface of the water by shooting drops of water at them," it overlooks the much more common and characteristic habit of stalking insects that are resting on plants in the water or at the water's edge. In reality, insects shot on the wing represent a very small percentage of the total food intake. In Siam, Toxotes was very rarely noticed in pursuit of flying insects. On the few occasions when I observed this habit, there had been an irruption of winged termites and the fish were very active in chasing the low-flying insects across a pond or water-course and directing a perfect barrage of shots if necessary to bring down the prey.

In *The Biology of Fishes* (1926), the author, H. M. Kyle, observed that "the taste for flies has become so great that one fish has developed into an expert sharp-shooter in stalking and smothering flies—with a drop of water and mucus." If "flies" can be interpreted as including ants, bees, termites, grasshoppers, moths, caterpillars, dragon-flies, beetles, cockroaches, ephemerids, and many other kinds of insects, as well as spiders, the statement is correct with the exception that insects are not smothered and there is no mucus in the watery pellet.

The range, accuracy, and force of the shooting powers of
Toxotes always excite surprise and admiration. In my experience in Siam the distance within which the fish could always
be depended upon to score a direct hit was three and a half
to four feet. A much longer effective range has been recorded.
Two fishes in the New York Aquarium could without difficulty
hit a small cockroach at a measured height of five feet above
the water.

Failure to hit a resting insect within proper range may be
due to movements of the vegetation or, in the case of a spider
dangling on a thread, to swaying caused by wind. When the
first shot misses a mark, other shots usually follow in quick succession.

The force with which the watery pellets may strike an
object is sometimes most astonishing to a human observer. An
insect may be knocked high in the air or may fall on the bank
beyond the fish's reach. At short range, the drops may strike
a person's face with a distinctly stinging sensation. On many
occasions, during exhibitions in Siam, a spider at the end of a
thread hanging from the end of a pole was knocked far up on
the thread or even over the pole. Spent shots could be heard to
splash against the roof of a veranda over the water.

The shooting habit begins to develop early and may be
observed in fish only an inch long. It is most amusing to see
the inexperienced youngsters sending out tiny drops which
may go only two or three inches. In half-grown fish the habit
is well developed, but the highest expression of the shooting
powers as regards accuracy, force, and range is to be seen only
in the fully matured fish.

A peculiar feeding trait was exhibited by both river fish
and pond fish in Siam when a spider on a thread was lowered
to within about one foot of the surface of the water. A fish,
which may have been shooting at the spider when it was two
or three feet distant, would with little apparent effort rise vertically from the water and seize the lure in its mouth, some-

orus J. and Margery J. Milne

The Praying Mantis matches his foliage so well that it easily ambushes flies, moths, and caterpillars.

(*See page 116.*)

THE BOLAS SPIDER

Hanging to the trapeze line by the legs of one side, she adjusts the casting line between her palpi and her long front leg and is then ready to hurl the viscid ball at her prey.

(*See page 132.*)

GLOWWORM CAVERN (Right)

Visitors must be quiet else the wary glowworms will turn off their lights.

(*See page 145.*)

*to by National Publicity Studios, Prime Minister's
Department, Wellington, New Zealand*

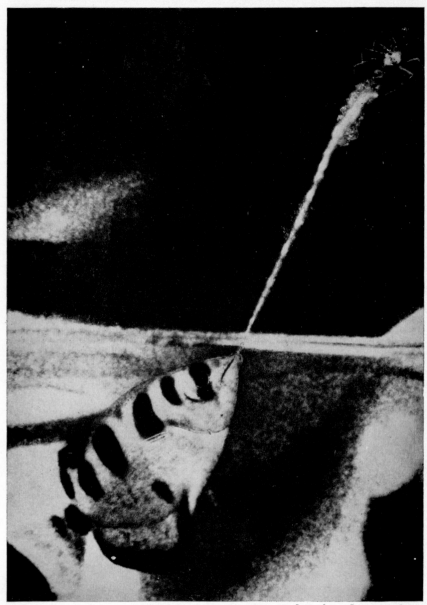

The Archer Fish makes its living by shooting insects with a drop or a short jet of water. Its aim is extremely accurate up to five feet, and shots that go wild carry ten to twelve feet. The insect may be knocked high in the air and fall back onto the water, or it may land on the bank out of reach.

(*See page 150.*)

When the odd-shaped tongue
ts against the roof of the mouth, a
ender tube is formed, which is less
1an a sixteenth of an inch in diam-
:er in a fish that is seven inches
mg.

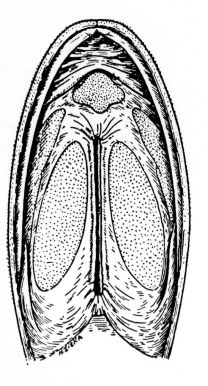

"Blow-pipe" of the Archer Fish.
The grooved tube that enables the
Archer Fish to project pellets of
water from its mouth is a narrow
slot in the roof of the mouth which
is closed by the tongue.

(See page 150.)

Compared to the poodle-like Alpaca (right), an adult Vicuña is a dainty, deer-like creature. However, its depressed ears are a warning that a wad of spittle is about to be sent in someone's direction.

(*See page 163.*)

Photo by Walter Henricks

Walker Van Riper photos

Here the superspeed camera catches the Trapdoor Spider in the act of seizing a beetle. If the trap door is lifted with a sliver of wood (*right*), the spider comes up to pull it down. (*See page 178.*)

Pygmy Man-o'-War Bird: an affectionate mother and youngster. The flimsy nest is on the trunk of a fallen Caesalpinia tree
at the remote Brazilian island of Trindade, in the South Atlantic.
(See page 185.)

times holding on when the line was raised several feet. This was done so readily and regularly as to suggest a normal habit, although as a matter of fact I never saw it tried on insects hovering near the surface or resting on plants. Probably spiders and caterpillars hanging from their threads are the principal victims of this method of attack.

The writer's acquaintance with this fish was formed in the Philippines, French Indo-China, Siam, Malaya, Burma, and India, but chiefly in Siam where it is common over most of the country and is called *pla sua,* or tiger fish, in allusion to the black crossbands on the yellow sides. Wild fish planted in a large pond in the compound of my residence in Bangkok were under close observation for a number of years and were a source of pleasure and instruction to myself and many foreign visitors and residents.

Among all the oriental fresh-water fishes with which I am acquainted in the wild state, none gives such an impression of intelligence and efficiency as does Toxotes. This impression grows on an observer as he notes the purposeful way in which a fish moves about in a stream, canal, or pond; the zeal and thoroughness with which it explores aquatic and overhanging land plants for insects; the high development of its sense of sight in both air and water; the skill displayed in dislodging insects and seizing them as they fall into the water; the alertness in avoiding danger; and the readiness in adapting itself to life in small ponds and responding to the attentions of persons who provide food.

A friend of mine, a distinguished scion of the royal family of Siam and an ardent student of fishes, had a residence on the broad Menam Chao Phya above Bangkok and used to entertain American and European guests with shooting-fish performances. A veranda on which he took many of his meals was directly over the water, and under it Toxotes could be found almost daily, attracted by scraps of fish, meat, chicken, and prawn that were regularly thrown from the table. By means of a spider or cricket dangled on a black thread from the end of a short bamboo pole, the shooting fish could readily be induced to display their marksmanship, and scores of foreign visitors, during the years I passed in Siam, were thus edified and amused. It was there that I sometimes saw spent watery pellets splash on the ceiling of the veranda ten to twelve feet above the river, and witnessed many other exhibitions that confirmed my respect for the intelligence and skill of Toxotes.

On two occasions to my personal knowledge, when my friend sat on the veranda eating his breakfast, reading a newspaper, smoking a cigarette, and apparently neglectful of his fish wards, his attention was attracted by well-directed shots which extinguished his cigarette.

🙠 THE VICUÑA'S GOLDEN FLEECE 🙠 *The little camel of the Andes with the finest wool in nature* 🙠 BY WALTER HENRICKS HODGE.

UNLIKE the mythical fleece of Jason, no sleepless dragon guards the haunts of the vicuña, the little Andean beast with the Golden Fleece. Nor need one be a mythological Jason to quest for this regal fleece. Yet only one person in every four million enjoys the beauty and warmth of fabrics woven from the golden-brown wool of the vicuña. Why? Because of scarcity of supply. Though the vicuña may become a plentiful animal under domestication, you may now have to pay upward of $1000 for a garment made of its wool! Little wonder that most people have never heard of the vicuña, a little camel that often has been called the prince of wool bearers.

This is unfortunate, for the fleece of this animal surpasses in fineness that of any other. A single vicuña hair is less than one-half the diameter of the hair of the finest strains of sheep. Beside it, a human hair would look like coarse wire. Indeed, vicuña is to wools what chinchilla is to furs. It is truly "the most beautiful textile fiber." It is not surprising that this golden fleece, so fine and so regal, was originally reserved exclusively for royalty—the Incas. At the time of the Conquest, the Spaniards had a royal quilt made as a gift for their sovereign, Philip II.

Vicuñas, like their close relatives the more familiar llamas, guanacos, and alpacas, are South American camels (Camelidae). Although camels are generally thought of as Old World animals, their ancestral dwelling place actually encompassed large parts of North America, on whose broad plains they developed in large numbers between 12 and 58 million years ago (Eocene to Miocene times). These prehistoric North

163

American camels looked more like their modern South American descendants than like the ungainly humped creatures of Africa and Asia. By the end of the great Ice Age (Pleistocene), camels became extinct in North America but not before they had migrated into the Old World and also into South America, where they evolved through the centuries into two now widely separate and superficially distinct types of creatures.

The vicuña (*Vicugna vicugna*) is the handsomest of our Western Hemisphere camels. It is also the smallest (only two and a half feet high at the shoulders) and the most graceful, being deerlike in appearance and movement. Despite its delicate appearance, the vicuña is actually the hardiest of the Andean camels. Llamas and guanacos cannot stay long at the bleak, blizzard-swept altitudes inhabited by these creatures. Only the alpaca can wander occasionally into these heights. Indeed, save for the rare little deer called *taruga*, vicuñas are the only large mammals in their mountaintop abode.

The vicuña's haunts include the veritable heights of the Andes. Only the line of perpetual snow and ice (which effectively bars the upward growth of animal pasturage) keeps this little camel from clambering above about 17,000 feet on the slopes of some of the loftiest peaks in this part of the world. Wedged in between the snow line on the one hand and the upper limits of crop cultivation on the other (approximately 14,000 feet) lies the belt that the vicuña can call home—a cloud-scraping homeland that averages considerably higher than the summits of Pike's Peak, Mt. Rainier, or the Matterhorn! This treeless land is called *puna*. It is a sort of Andean tundra, with extensive rock fields or semibare earth. It supports sparse bunch grasses called *ichu*, curious mounds of cushion plants, and, in the poorly drained hollows, vivid green moors of short rushes. These moors serve the vicuñas for herbage, and it is around them that the animals are most frequently seen, particularly in the dry season (April to December).

Today one can climb by automobile into many parts of the puna country, and if lucky, one can catch a fleeting glimpse of these "substratosphere" camels. But to stalk them away from the road across the high pampas is another matter. Even on the level, the breath of the average person, in an atmosphere drained of life-giving oxygen, comes in short gasps. *Soroche,* or mountain sickness, except for the barrel-chested, big-hearted highland Indians, is an ever-present worry. Like the Indian, the vicuña is attuned physically to life at high elevation. So specialized is this creature that if transferred to sea level it often sickens and dies.

One might think that in a treeless area where the highest bunch-grass clump is scarcely two feet high, vicuñas would be easy to see. On the contrary, except when in motion or when silhouetted against the sky, they are practically invisible, so well does the color of their fleece blend into the perennially-drab brownish aspect of the puna.

The coats of llamas and alpacas, through endless selection in domestication, have become diversified so that one sees various combinations of browns, blacks, grays, and whites. But the undomesticated vicuña has only a single constant color pattern. This is so beautiful a gradation of hues that when fabricated it is rarely dyed. Rich chestnut-brown is the dominant color covering the upper parts of the head, neck, back, flanks, and legs. As it passes to the underparts, this hue is diluted to a soft, golden fawn color and finally to white on the belly and the inside of the thighs. Also light is the short wool of the jaws and face. But perhaps the most striking feature of the adult animal is the conspicuous ruff of long, soft, white hair which, partially surrounding the base of the slim neck, falls down over the chest and makes the dainty forelegs appear to project from wispy plumes of wool, giving an almost birdlike aspect. The white ruff is a sign of maturity and is lacking in lamb vicuñas, which, however, show signs of where the ruff is to appear. Moreover, lambkin vicuñas are much lighter in color—all fawn

—and softer coats than theirs are hardly imaginable. They surpass in fineness and silkiness even those of their parents, a fact that was put to practical use by the ancient Peruvians, who made special fabrics from such fleeces. Alpaca hair also varies according to age, sex, and location, and some alpaca hair is actually finer than the thicker vicuña hair.

On the puna, vicuñas run in small groups of from six to twelve animals. These are all females and young except for the leader, which is a vigorous male. Over a century ago, the distinguished Swiss zoologist Von Tschudi ably described the daily activity of such a vicuña family group: "Whilst the females are quietly grazing, the male stands at the distance of some paces apart and carefully keeps guard over them. At the approach of danger he gives a signal, consisting of a sort of whistling sound and a quick movement of the foot. Immediately the herd draws closely together, each animal anxiously stretching out its head in the direction of the threatening danger. They then take flight; first moving leisurely and cautiously, then quickening their pace to the utmost degree of speed; whilst the male vicuña, who covers the retreat, frequently halts to observe the movements of the enemy. The females, with singular fidelity and affection, reward the watchful care of their protector. If he is wounded or killed, they gather round him in a circle, uttering their shrill tones of lamentation, and they will suffer themselves to be captured or killed rather than desert him by pursuing their flight. The neigh of the vicuna, like that of the other animals of its class, resembles a short, sharp whistle. But when the shrill sound vibrates through the pure puna air, the practiced ear can readily distinguish the cry of the vicuña from that of the other animals of the same family."

Von Tschudi might have added that, like many wild things, vicuñas seem to have a big bump of curiosity, which undoubtedly has led more than one to its demise. Upon the approach of anything strange, instead of running straight away, they lope off a bit and turn to observe. If no danger is apparent, they generally approach cautiously and linger for a long while. The writer, when traveling by car, has more than once come upon such a group. They seemed to consider the automobile inoffensive, in fact worthy of investigation. But as soon as a person stepped out, the group would hurry off over the horizon. Their fleetness has been their safety. This, together with the absence of firearms among the highland Indians and the stringent laws that supposedly protect them, accounts for their survival today. For certainly an animal with a golden fleece so valuable would long since have been exterminated in the centuries following the Spanish Conquest.

Actually, the vicuña was better protected before the conquest of Peru than it is today—protected by this hemisphere's (and possibly the world's) original conservationists, the Incas. Their civilization recognized the value of vicuñas—and all other game—and enacted laws accordingly. These laws worked, too, for under the Incas anyone molesting one of these little camels, except in one of the orderly state-run hunts, was subject to death. One might say that the vicuña was a royal animal. Dainty vicuña figurines were wrought in gold, silver, and stone; and vicuña fleece was woven into fabrics reserved only for the nobility.

Vicuña fabric of any sort was called *cumpi* by the Incas. Much of it was woven by men, the so-called *cumpi-camayoc-cuna*, on curious upright looms that have long since disappeared. Certain types of *cumpi* were better than others, that from lambkin vicuña surpassing that from adult fleece. The finest *cumpi* was woven by the chosen women (*aclla-cuna*) or Virgins of the Sun, the Incas' handwomen. It is even said that they improved it with the even silkier hair from bats, of all things. But little credence can be placed in this story, because the longest fur from any Peruvian bat is only 7 or 8 mm. in length, and spinning such a short staple by hand would be impossible.

Vicuña wool, in preparation for thread making, was washed in water but never thoroughly. The natural animal oils were valued, in combination with the spinner's saliva applied by the thumb and forefinger, to produce a woolen thread that was remarkably pliable and smooth. The ancient process of thread making has been handed down to the modern Indians, and wherever one sees them, even when they are backpacking burdens or children, one may spot the ever-present distaff and whirling spindle.

From the hands of the chosen women of ancient Peru have come some of the finest wool textiles ever made anywhere in the whole world. Before Europeans reached South America, thread was being spun and woven by Andean Indians into tapestries so fine as to show a weft count of 350 weft threads to the inch. Yet the best that modern man has been able to produce from fine vicuña wool is a weft count of 90! The rarity of true vicuña weavings is shown by the fact that, although there is no doubt of their existence in ancient times, we know of no unquestionable example among the collections in museums. Many pieces have not been subjected to the specialized microscopic analysis that is necessary to ascertain the identity of vicuña hair, but the ones that have, have proved to be alpaca. Unfortunate it is that such a luxury art as that of *cumpi* weaving was suppressed by the Spaniards and its technique of manufacture lost through the centuries, perhaps forever.

In Inca times vicuña wool was obtained systematically during one of the great public hunts called *cako* or *chacu*, sporting events that were held periodically and served not only to reduce the surplus game but also to increase the meat supply. We have an authentic account of one of these imperial hunts, for one was organized in honor of Pizarro by Manco Inca. In this particular hunt more than 10,000 Indian beaters surrounded an area approximately 50 miles in circumference. Closing in gradually, they drove all encircled animals into a common center, and when the human net was tight enough and small enough, designated hunters entered to kill the animals required. Of the animals thus trapped, only the vicuñas were ordinarily taken alive and shorn, presumably being hog-tied during the process. Simple bronze or copper knives, the only metal tools available, were probably used in the shearing. And even today a simple knife is the shearing implement of the highland Indian in vicuñaland.

Did the Incas attempt the domestication of this beast with the golden fleece? As they had no written language, we can only say we do not know. But since ancient Peruvians domesticated the closely related alpaca and llama, we might guess that they tried to tame the vicuña and failed. Or, since vicuña wool was reserved for the royalty, perhaps it was better left a relative rarity to be obtained from the wild only through the medium of the public hunt.

With the conquest of the Incas by Europeans, all their strict and able conservation practices failed. The Conquistadores could scarcely believe that the fine vicuña textiles that fell to their plundering hands were made from a wool. Instead they thought it was some New World kind of silk. As with the other riches of Peru, greed got the best of the conquerors. No sooner had they learned of the true source of this New World "silk" than slaughter of vicuñas became wanton. The animals shortly approached the verge of extinction, if one is to believe the writers of the time. By the beginning of the nineteenth century, the time of Peruvian independence, the stock of these little camels had been so decimated that Bolivar enacted a decree in 1825 prohibiting their killing. The Liberator further offered prizes—without success—for the vicuña's domestication.

Compared with Inca times, the vicuña population was sadly depleted, but possibly it is erroneous to say it was on the verge of extinction. For there are so many isolated, uninhabited *refugia* in the high puna country, even today, that to kill all the vicuñas would seem to be next to impossible. Von

Tschudi, who was certainly a careful scientific observer, noted about this time (1838-1842) that "frequent hunting seems not to have the effect of diminishing the numbers of these animals . . ." In the altos, he said, they were still found in vast numbers. The same writer took part in a variation of the old Inca hunt, which apparently is still promoted today, occasionally and furtively, by the highland Aymara Indians of the Titicaca area. Von Tschudi's description is worth quoting:

"In this curious hunt, one man at least belonging to each family in the puna villages takes a part, and women accompany the train, to officiate as cooks to the hunters. The whole company, frequently amounting to seventy or eighty individuals, proceeds to the altos (the most secluded parts of the puna), which are the haunts of the vicuñas. They take with them stakes and a great quantity of rope and cord. A spacious open plain is selected, and the stakes are driven into the ground in a circle, at intervals of from twelve to fifteen feet apart, and are connected together by ropes fastened to them at the height of two or two-and-a-half feet from the ground. The circular space within the stakes is about half a league in circumference, and an opening of about two hundred paces in width is left for entrance. On the ropes by which the stakes are fastened together the women hang pieces of colored rags, which flutter about in the wind.

"The *chacu* being fully prepared, the men, some of whom are mounted on horseback, range about within a circuit of several miles, driving before them all the herds of vicuñas they meet with, and forcing them into the chacu. When a sufficient number of vicuñas is collected, the entrance is closed. The timid animals do not attempt to leap over the ropes, being frightened by the fluttering rags suspended from them and, when thus secured, the Indians easily kill them by the *bolas*. These bolas consist of three balls, composed either of lead or stone; two of them heavy and the third rather lighter. They are fastened to long elastic strings, made of twisted sinews of the vicuña, and the opposite ends of the strings are all tied together. The Indian holds the lightest of the three balls in his hand, and swings the two others in a wide circle above his head; then, taking his aim at the distance of about fifteen or twenty paces, he lets go the handball, upon which all the three balls whirl in a circle and twine round the object aimed at. The aim is usually taken at the hind legs of the animals, and the cords twisting around them they become firmly bound. It requires great skill and long practice to throw the bolas dexterously, especially when on horseback: a novice in the art incurs the risk of dangerously hurting either himself or his horse, by not giving the balls the proper swing, or by letting go the hand-ball too soon.

"The vicuñas, after being secured by the bolas, are killed, and the flesh is distributed in equal portions among the hunters. The skins belong to the Church." The chacu hunt described by Von Tschudi took place in the altos of Huayhuay, and during the five days of the hunt, 122 vicuñas were caught.

During the hundred years since Bolivar first acted to conserve the vicuña, protective laws have been sporadically reenacted by the Peruvian government. Rigid control of hunting is impossible in a country without game wardens, but these laws are certainly a step in the right direction. As recently as 1940, a decree was passed prohibiting the killing of vicuñas or the possession of any articles made from their skin or wool. That the law has its infractions may be judged from the fact that a traveler in puna territory may easily, if at times furtively, acquire articles from the natives such as vicuña-skin robes, hats made of vicuña felt, or vicuña woolens. Although obtainable, they are difficult to get out of the country except with official permits. Moreover, nearly every highland village boasts of one or more tame vicuñas, animals usually captured as lambs (when a female is killed) and then reared as pets.

Despite these minor infractions of the law, the vicuña is fortunately not uncommon today in some places, especially in the outlying fringes of the altiplano. Although listed in 1942 as a vanishing mammal of the Western Hemisphere, the present status of this little camel is hardly that. In Peru alone, estimates of the wild vicuña population run from a conservative (and more probable) fifty thousand animals to an optimistic million. These figures are little more than guesses.

Modern Peruvians are showing signs of accomplishing what the ancient people failed to achieve—the domestication of this beast with the Golden Fleece. If practical, this should bring a new and profitable industry. Several large private haciendas in Peru's state of Puno already have small experimental flocks of vicuñas for husbandry study. Most of these animals were captured by running them down on the puna with horses, a difficult job. Peru's National Board of Wool Industry is behind these studies. Even with abundant terrain for their project, problems still exist. Though easily and frequently tamed, vicuñas usually refuse to breed in captivity, thus making the building up of a commercial flock most difficult. But if given ample space, simulating wild conditions, it has been found that vicuñas may breed within a fenced area.

Sizable flocks are needed, because the little beasts produce only about a third of a pound of fine wool per adult animal. About a third of this represents the longer beard hair comprising the vicuña's outer coat—useless in fine textile manufacture. The remaining two thirds, about a quarter of a pound all told, is the silklike inner hair yielding the stock for fine vicuña fabric. Thus the annual wool production from a pioneer flock of 300 domesticated vicuñas is only 100 pounds, barely enough to make half a dozen fine coats. No wonder yardage of vicuña fabrics is valued in the hundreds of dollars! To increase the wool production, experiments have been made in crossing the vicuña with its cousin the alpaca, the most important of South America's "camels" as far as wool production is concerned. Such hybridizing has been successful, and the hardy progeny of these crosses, known as paco-vicuñas, show the heavy wool production of alpacas with some of the finer characteristics of vicuñas. Unfortunately, the characteristics of the original cross do not hold in succeeding generations, the wool decreasing in value to such an extent that hybridizing has been given up.

Widespread vicuña domestication may still be a thing of the future, but it must eventually come. Highland Peru and Bolivia can well afford to develop a luxury industry such as this. Once the civilized world has seen the superb qualities of vicuña wool, a market will surely develop for fabrics originating from this prince of wool bearers, the little Andean camel with the Golden Fleece.

❧ THE FOUR-EYED FISH ❧ *It sees both above and below the water—at the same time* ❧ BY G. KINGSLEY NOBLE, LATE CURATOR, EXPERIMENTAL BIOLOGY, THE AMERICAN MUSEUM OF NATURAL HISTORY.

GREAT interest was aroused when two pairs of the famous four-eyed fish were brought to the American Museum alive. These were procured in southern Mexico by Mr. T. McDougall, a distinguished naturalist who had traveled extensively in that region. The specimens represented the species *Anableps dowii,* the most attractive of the genus.

The optical equipment that enables this fish to see in the air as well as in the water makes it unique in the whole series of backboned animals. Inhabiting waters that are often so muddy that objects cannot be seen for any distance, it swims almost continuously at the surface with its "air-eyes" thrust above and its "water-eyes" directed downward. It has specialized in feeding on the floating material that it encounters in its wanderings in the dual realm of air and water.

Although *Anableps,* as the fish is technically called, has been mentioned frequently in the writings of naturalists for a century and a half, it is still one of the rarest species in aquaria. There are very few records of the fish having reached northern aquaria alive, and fewer still of its having lived there for more than a short time. The four *Anableps* that Mr. McDougall collected and with great trouble brought to the Museum were installed in one of the large tanks in the greenhouse on the roof of the African Building. These "queer fish" proved a very important addition to the collection of live animals under observation in the biological laboratory.

The double pair of eyes that *Anableps* has developed have

an important bearing on the evolution of vertebrate animals from water to land-creatures. Perhaps the most stupendous step in the entire evolutionary change from fish to man occurred when a certain group of fishes living in the drying pools of Devonian times had to adapt themselves to life on land. This change, which took place probably 400,000,000 years ago, involved a tremendous reorganization affecting many parts of the bodies of the animals undergoing it. For the moment we may consider only the eyes.

The fishes which left their pools for an unknown world of dry land and sunshine had to make over their short-sighted eyes into structures that could see objects accurately at a distance. Water is relatively opaque, and distant vision is consequently not possible in this medium. On land, ability to see objects at a distance was not only possible but necessary. The changes in the eye that were occasioned by the new existence on dry land were more complex than might be supposed. The lens of a fish's eye is large and spherical, and for distant vision in the air the lens had to be flattened, reduced in size, and moved back from the cornea. How this was actually accomplished we shall never know, since the soft parts of animals are not preserved as fossils.

What we do know, however, is that the first land vertebrates, having evolved directly from fish, were devoid of necks. In order to secure an unobstructed view, they had to develop muscles to periscope their eyes above the surface of their heads. The eye in dry atmosphere, further, had somehow to be kept moist. The first land vertebrates therefore gradually gained protective eyelids and glandular mechanisms which would keep the cornea moist and yet free from dirt.

The reptiles early made an advance over the first land vertebrates in developing special muscles to change the form of the lens by pressure from the outside. The birds in turn improved on this compressing mechanism considerably. As a result, a recently hatched chick may have its eye focussed on a worm in front of it and in a moment throw the head back to focus on a passing hawk.

The mammals, which sprang from a different group of reptiles, evolved an entirely different mechanism for rapidly changing the focus of the eye. When at rest, the mammalian eye is far-sighted like that of the first land vertebrates, but the lens is flatter than that of the Amphibia and it is held in place by a series of delicate fibers which keep it flattened. As we grow older the lenses of our eyes lose their elasticity and the delicate fibers holding them can no longer change the curvature of the lenses. Hence, our eyes do not focus as efficiently as in youth.

Anableps has none of these special devices of reptiles, birds, and mammals to change the form of the lens. Its aerial eye merely represents the first stage in the evolution of vision in the air. *Anableps* was confronted with the problem of developing eyes for vision above the surface while at the same time it could not afford to give up its water-eyes entirely. Nature in this dilemma modified half of each eye for vision above the

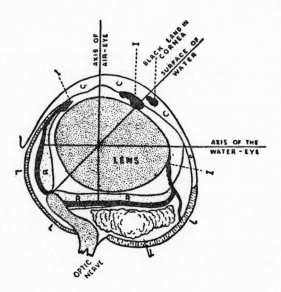

surface while retaining the other half for duty below the surface.

During the early years of the last century the four-eyed fish attracted the attention of the great anatomists who studied the wealth of animal life sent to Europe from the British, French, and Dutch colonies in northern South America. As long ago as 1803, a German anatomist, Schneider, very accurately described the structure of the fish's two pairs of optical equipment. Even at that time, it had been established that the four-eyed fish has only one pair of eyes and that each eye is divided by an opaque band into upper and lower sections, the former adapted for vision in the air and the latter for gazing under water. Each pupil is divided in two by ingrowth of the iris. For distant vision, a lens must be well back of the cornea, while for close viewing, the lens must be in the reverse position. *Anableps* has only one pair of lenses, but they accomplish this double function by being egg-shaped, with the long axis directed into the water and the short one into the air.

The "air-eye" is not equipped with glands to keep it moist in the dry atmosphere. Consequently, the fish must frequently dip its eyes below the surface. McDougall observed the creatures in their native haunts ducking their heads below the surface, and he guessed correctly the reason for this habit. Apparently no other naturalists who have studied *Anableps* in the field have called attention to this habit.

Nor has anyone previously noted that the lower pupil is shielded by a double shade formed by the projecting parts of the iris. This double screen no doubt prevents surface-reflection from striking into the lower pupil. The accompanying sketch of the eye of a living fish shows the lower pupil-screen in normal position.

All species of *Anableps* have the strange bifocal eyes which, far from being merely a curiosity of nature, actually show us an important stage in the evolution of the eyes of higher forms, including our own.

THE TRAP-DOOR SPIDER *It lives alone in a dugout that is almost undetectable* BY WILLIS J. GERTSCH, CURATOR, DEPARTMENT OF INSECTS AND SPIDERS, THE AMERICAN MUSEUM OF NATURAL HISTORY.

ONE MOMENT you see it, the next it is gone. The spider seems to have been swallowed up by the earth without leaving a sign on the surface to show where it has gone. Tens of thousands of years before soldiers were constructing dugouts and pill-boxes, the trap-door spiders had learned to make excellent ones for themselves. Not only are these subterranean fortresses impregnable to most enemies, but the trap-door lid often fits so perfectly as to make them practically gas proof. Man's attempts to hide his dugouts by grooming the soil and rearranging the vegetation are feeble efforts compared with those of the spider, who is a master of camouflage.

Intensive hunting during the day may not lead to the discovery of the spider and its nest, for it is a most secretive creature. Sometimes at night, under the rays of the head lamp, it may be seen at the mouth of the burrow, supporting the trap door on its back; or it may be bold enough to venture a few inches away from the opening. When disturbed, it performs its surprising disappearing act with lightning quickness, leaving the would-be investigator at least momentarily confounded. It takes a keen eye and considerable experience to locate the door, which often blends so completely with the soil as to be virtually invisible.

Much of the adventure in the life of a trap-door spider is crowded into the first few days of freedom when the young spiderling, having deserted the protection of the maternal burrow, strikes out for itself or in company with its numer-

178

ous brothers and sisters. It is in the early spring that the urge to move impels the babes to climb upon a promontory from which they will make their first, and probably their last, aerial flight.

"Ballooning" is a habit that is associated with spiders of all or nearly all families, and it is now well known that trap-door spiders, children of the earth for most of their life, are no exception to the rule. The young of *Pachylomerus* travel overland in single file in a group toward a sizable tree or other tall object, leaving behind them as the record of their march a narrow, silken band. Up the tree they go, often to a considerable height, and when all is in readiness they tilt up their abdomens, throw out silken threads to the breezes, and are wafted away.

How far they fly depends upon the air currents, which sometimes support them for many miles but ordinarily probably drop them to earth after a flight of only a few rods. Ballooning is interpreted as a protective habit, for the dispersion of the numerous progeny on the whims of the winds prevents a wholesale cannibalism and effects a more general distribution of the animals over suitable terrain.

Once the baby spider is again on the ground, the wanderlust deserts it and it digs a tiny burrow into the soil, comparable in all respects except size with that of the mother, and caps the opening with a hinged cover. For a digging instrument the true trap-door spider is equipped with a comb-like rake of short, stout spines on the margins of the jaws. Using the silk from the spinnerets to bind the grains together, the spider carries bits of soil outside the burrow and deposits them at some distance from the opening. The walls of the tube are waterproofed with saliva and earth, so that the surface becomes smooth and firm, and are then lined with silk.

With the establishment of a domicile, the spider becomes antisocial, an individualist jealous of its tiny home, which it defends with glistening fangs. Its brothers and sisters, so recently tolerated as equals in the maternal burrow and as companions on the march to the ballooning tree, become fair prey to its jaws should they come within range.

When the growing spider outgrows its burrow, it enlarges it by cutting and scraping off bits of soil with the rake and carrying them away from the site. Rocks imbedded in the soil may oblige the spider to dig a new tunnel in a more favorable situation. It rarely deserts its burrow voluntarily. When it is forcibly removed, it will accept the unoccupied tunnel of another spider, remodeling it if necessary. During the growing period when the spider is remodeling and strengthening its closed tube, it is less subject to the attacks of marauding wasps which, in filling the food requirements for their offspring, pass up the smaller burrows with their inferior occupants in favor of mature or nearly mature prey.

Although spiders of many other families burrow, the trap-door spiders have far outstripped them in the excellence of their tunneling. They have become specialists who dig with better instruments, line with greater care, and are the originators of the intriguing practice of capping the burrows with a perfect lid. The trap door is not a unique accomplishment of these spiders, for it has been developed independently in several other groups, but the finished product of the trap-door spiders bespeaks a mastery not closely approached by emulators.

The typical burrow, a cylindrical tunnel in the earth which is completely lined with silk, is spacious enough in part of its length to allow the spider to reverse its position at will. Within its confines the spider will find a haven until life ends in insidious, violent, or natural death. What are the advantages of the burrow, which has become such a dominant element in the lives of these spiders? In the first place it is the property of a single, unsocial individual and can become, with the passage of time, more and more adequately coated with silk, more and more familiar in its every part, and thus in-

creasingly acceptable to the spider. It is a retreat from the rays
of the sun, the extreme heat of which is shunned by nocturnal
and diurnal spiders as well. The hinged lid prevents rain and
surface water from entering, thus keeping it dryer than situa-
tions on the surface. All of the burrowing spiders live more
than a single year, some of them several years, so the tunnel
is effective in tempering the extremes of inclement weather.
During the hottest part of the summer, and strangely enough
at a time when some parasitic wasps are present in their maximum number, the opening may be closed tightly with earth
and silk. The tube beneath the surface is cooler during the
summer heat and somewhat warmer during the extreme winter
cold.

Relatively inconspicuous in any case, the burrow opening
is often well hidden, and may be made even more difficult to
discern through the efforts of the spider. Mosses, leaves,
sticks, and other debris are placed to advantage on the lid
and around the entrance, the result, to our eyes at least, hint-
ing of camouflage. When in active use, the burrow can serve
as an ambush from which the spider rushes out to seize its
prey. And once an insect is caught, the nest becomes in many
cases the dining room. At the proper season, the burrow may
become the mating chamber; and within its confines occur
egg laying and cocooning. Later it is the home of the young
spiderlings for some time after their emergence from the egg-
sac.

The opening to the surface is the spider's only contact with
the outside. Allowing the spider to be menaced only from one
direction, the burrow can be defended either from the mouth
or from within the tube by strong jaws. Above ground the trap-
door spider's inferior sensory equipment would place it at a
much greater disadvantage in combat with its specialized
enemies.

While the demands for privacy have probably inspired the
perfection of the underground castle of the trap-door spider,

it is more intriguing to think of the domicile in terms of response to the ravages of some arch enemy. By far the most fearsome assailant of the animal is the spider wasp, a common name used in reference to various species of Pompilidae which are exclusively spider predators. Other enemies may wreak their toll in an insidious way and possibly destroy as many individuals as do the wasps, but the gleaming tyrant is a predator of the first magnitude, which in hand-to-hand struggle takes its toll of adult or large spiders.

The wasp actively forages over the soil and is unerringly directed to the site by a sense not conditioned by previous experience. It arrives at the trap door beneath which sits its prospective victim. The spider, possibly informed of the presence of an intruder by its delicate tactile sense, may be fully prepared to resist to the death. If unprepared, or if resistance is finally broken down, the spider may quickly find itself confronted by an enemy that has lifted the trap door or gnawed through it and entered the spacious burrow. The struggle that ensues is not a battle of giants. It is a very unequal one, from which the wasp almost always emerges the victor. Swift and sure in her movements, liberally endowed with fine sensory equipment and armed with a deadly sting, the wasp faces a larger creature which, though at best advantage in the prepared battle ground of the deeper recess of the burrow, is not a fair match. After a brief struggle, during which the wasp paralyzes the spider with venom from its fiery sting, an egg is deposited on the abdomen, from which will hatch the voracious larva. Doomed to lie helpless while furnishing fresh food for the larva, virtually dead if not actually so, the once high spider finds its castle converted into a crypt. Its industrial skill has failed to make the burrow impregnable to its most formidable enemy.

It is not generally known that there are many different kinds of trap-door spiders in the United States, probably as many as 20 species. They differ to a considerable degree in general appearance and are often distinctive in their habits. Most of the species are confined to the southern portions of our country. All of them close the opening to the burrow with some sort of lid; yet within the burrow itself may occur various innovations. Although it must be confessed that we know all too little about the habits of these secretive creatures, it is intriguing to try to interpret the burrows in terms of protection for the occupants.

The California trap-door spider, *Bothriocyrtum californicum,* builds a thick door, made up of alternating layers of soil and silk and beveled to fit into the burrow opening, much as a cork fits into a bottle. The burrow, capped with the thick door, which is heavy enough to close of its own weight, is ordinarily a single tube. When menaced, the spider holds the door down with claws and fangs with surprising strength. Even man, with the aid of an instrument such as a knife blade or other tool, has great difficulty in forcing the "cork" door. Physical strength is a definite asset in the spider's efforts to keep its home inviolate.

On the other hand, the lid may be made up almost wholly of silk and lie loosely rather than fitting snugly into the aperture. Dubbed a "wafer" door because it is not substantial enough to impede an intruder for long, being soft and pliable and not heavy enough to close of its own weight, this type of door seems not to be defensible by strength alone. As an innovation, *Myrmekiaphila,* the spider that spins this type of door, has within the main burrow a secret side chamber, likewise closed with a trap door, into which it retreats and which it defends by holding it fast against the silken wall of the main tube. It is quite possible that this sort of strategy is sufficient in some cases to confound the predator.

Still another type of defense is presented by *Cyclocosmia,* a curious trap-door spider whose abdomen is round and leathery, forming a flattened disk behind. When disturbed, *Cyclocosmia* retreats head downward to the innermost recess of the tube to a point where the hard disk of the abdomen fits it perfectly, plugging it like a stopper. The coriaceous abdomen is so tough that no predator is able to get to the vulnerable part of the spider while it maintains this position.

Thus, the trap-door spiders—pioneers in the art of hiding their burrows and capping them with a tough, movable door—have contrived to protect their homes by some of the most extraordinary devices to be found anywhere in the animal kingdom.

☙ MAN-O'-WAR BIRD *☙* *A corsair that spends
most of its life in the air* *☙* BY ROBERT CUSHMAN
MURPHY, CHAIRMAN, DEPARTMENT OF BIRDS, AMERICAN
MUSEUM OF NATURAL HISTORY.

A SEA FOWL that cannot swim; a fish-eater that never touches
water save with the tip of its bill; a glider equipped with elon-
gate planes but devoid of landing gear with which to take off
or return on any level surface; a being with the pinions of a
dark angel, the insignificant feet of a hummingbird, the code
of a buccaneer—such is the frigate-bird or man-o'-war.

The ocean is its larder, but its true home is the sky; no other
bird spends so large a proportion of its life aloft on idling
wings. From Cancer to Capricorn stretches the broad belt of
its range, with extensions nearer the poles at mid-ocean islands
and wherever a Gulf Stream or its counterpart tempers the
shore waters of middle latitudes. Solomon's sailors must have
encountered it as their quinquiremes pulled toward Ophir;
ancient Greek adventurers to the Arabian Sea called it the
souspha and recognized it as the most aerial of birds. Columbus saw it on September 29, 1492, thirteen days before the
landfall at San Salvador, and entered in his journal an inspired record of its piratical behavior. Modern voyagers know
it throughout the warmer oceans of the globe, because from
Florida and Texas to Brazil and the Cape of Good Hope and
India, from Mexico to Hawaii, Peru and Australia, it finds a
base on nearly every dry speck in the sea and forages along
all shores including the busiest of tropical seaports.

Corsairs by well-deserved reputation, the man-o'-war birds
are capable, when it pleases them, of earning their own living
as honestly as any fisherman. In the South Atlantic I have seen
six of them hovering in a row, with a slow beating of majestic

185

wings, above a shoal of surface fish. Thus poised close to
choppy water, they would strike downward, swinging their
long beaks like scimitars beneath their breasts, the hooked
tips each time deftly seizing a small fish. Every bird caught
three or four a minute and yet left the school oblivious of the
toll taken from its ranks.

More often, however, the man-o'-war rides high, spies its
prey from afar, and makes its capture by the sheer speed
of a power-dive rather than by subtlety. A fledgling sooty tern
squatting on the pebbles far from the shelter and protection
of the bay-cedars, a baby sea-turtle working toward the water
from its incubator in the hot sand, a herring that incautiously
reflects the sunbeams from its silver scales, a flying fish shooting from the blue sea before the dash of an albacore—they are
all fair game to the man-o'-war. Nose-diving from the sky, with
a whistle of wind through stiff quills, the animate bolt descends
in unerring pursuit, flattens out in the last split second to avoid
a crash or a breathless plunge beneath the waves, tosses its
victim in mid-air so that it will slide down the smooth way,
and then mounts with long sweeps of the wings back to its
vantage level. There is something peculiarly dramatic in the
plight of the flying-fish—driven into the air by a bigger fish
that cannot fly only to find a grave in the belly of a bird that
cannot swim!

Such are the usual habits of the flying angler during rough
or blustery weather. Its better-known technique of banditry
is reserved chiefly for lazy periods of calms and gentle trade
winds, when it seems to express the traditional Anglo-Saxon
sporting sentiment: "It's a fine day; let's go out and kill something." Strictly speaking, killing is not its aim at such times
but, as among all pirates, torture and maiming enter when
necessary into its persuasive methods.

Other sea fowl, especially the fish-catching boobies of various species which share its range throughout the world, become unwilling slaves of the man-o'-war, whose real purpose

is to appropriate goods amassed by the sweat of other brows. At such times the man-o'-war keeps a knowing eye on its neighbors instead of the ocean. Singling out a homebound booby that fatuously rejoices in a full crop, the rakish freebooter gives chase, following with dexterous agility every dodge and turn of the hapless runaway, and sticking like Nemesis until the booby disgorges in air. Then the robber tips forward to snatch the secondhand prize, which rarely has time to reach the water. But if mere unrelenting, contemptuous pursuit proves an insufficient threat, the man-o'-war is ready enough to add the cruel goad of its bill. Stubbornness on the part of a booby may lead to a torn neck or a dislocated leg. In the booby colonies one can often find cripples that attest the wrath of the implacable tyrant.

The female man-o'-war bird is always larger than her mate and is by all odds the boss of the family, even though the male displays an exclusive badge of masculinity in the form of an expansible throat sac. During the breeding season this is inflated by a series of pumping, gulping actions until it attains the size and appearance of a red toy balloon. It is then the love banner that produces the requisite excitement in the female, who alights on the tangled tops of shrubbery or swamp trees that the male has chosen for a nest. Both birds next assume a backward-leaning posture, face to face, raise their bills, allow their wings to droop limply, wave their heads and roll their bodies ecstatically while emitting incoherent gurgling and chuckling noises. At the same time the pointed, iridescent feathers on the back stand up like bristles and the lovers swell and tremble with an amorous ardor, of which the gorgeous red globe of the male is the most striking symbol. Despite all this mutuality of courtship, however, the major burden of home-care, including incubation and the brooding of the chick, falls to the lot of henpecked father.

Both birds of a pair take part in nest-building, the female toting lumber while the male, with his rubber throat blown up, squats on the platform under construction, arranges the incoming sticks and, what is more important, protects them against pilfering by strange females. He dare not leave his post at this critical juncture because "finding is keeping" in the morality of the tribe. Sisters, aunts, and other men's wives swoop down on an unguarded nest and purloin every vestige within a twinkling. Ordinarily the twigs are snapped off in passing flight from the tips of dead branches, or are filched from the red-footed boobies—the only species of its kind that uses wood or builds above the ground—while they are carrying them homeward for their own domestic purpose. The alacrity with which the boobies yield to the highwaymen might lead an observer to suppose that the sacrifice of a stick is a means of saving their dinners.

The last would hardly be a sound conclusion, however, for breeding ground and feeding ground are two different worlds in the philosophy of the man-o'-war bird. The sea is for plunder, the nest for peaceful family life; at home the Jolly Roger is furled, the cutlass sheathed. When nest-building is finished, the men-o'-war covering their eggs or youngsters become the most mild-mannered of sea fowl. Not only do they sit inoffensively when a man approaches and touches them but, moreover, toward their dear companions, the boobies, they behave as though nothing had ever happened to mar the eternal friendship between the two! Indeed, nesting boobies and man-o'-war birds a yard apart pay rather less attention to each other than either would to fellow members of its own species. All of which goes to show how fully the reactions of birds are determined by the particular stimulus of the moment, which retains no meaning in their consciousness after that moment has passed.

The man-o'-war bird's personal troubles stem mostly from its own awkwardness anywhere out of the air. There are hazards aplenty for such nearly legless creatures among the limbs of sea-grape and mangrove. The birds sometimes lose their

balance and, before they can launch into flight, slither helplessly down the branches into the jaws of crocodiles or to a
lingering death made certain by their inability to clamber
out of the tangles to some jumping-off place. Furthermore,
many an adult has been hanged by the neck in a crotch. Experiments with captured man-o'-war birds have shown that
they are unable to fly among shrubbery. Birds placed on the
ground, or tossed into the air a little above the ground, between
bay-cedars at the Dry Tortugas Islets were quite incapable
of making a getaway unless they had a clearance of at least
eight feet, and then only when they were flying into the wind.
Nearly everywhere their nests are built at an elevation that
provides some sort of spring-off from which the birds can
take flight. In a very few localities, such as Boatswain-bird
Islet, off Ascension, in the tropical Atlantic, where the egg
is laid on bare, stony soil, they may find it simpler merely to
tumble into space from the brink of the adjacent cliff.

The ordinary tree nest is nothing to boast about for the
safety of the single offspring. When an incubating parent takes
flight, it sometimes bowls the egg off with itself. Daylight
shows through the flimsy structure which, however, later
becomes more firmly matted together by the droppings of the
voracious youngster, clinging as tight as a limpet to its cradle.
In its early stages the chick must be carefully shielded by a
parent from the curdling heat of the equatorial sun. Subsequently, when quills sprout through its fluffy white down, it
faces a second perilous trial, for the quantity of blood in the
shafts of fast-growing feathers weighs it flat, head and limbs,
so that for several days its utter dejection and listlessness make
it seem more dead than alive.

Thus far I have spoken as though there were but one man-
o'-war, instead of many kinds. It is only a few years, indeed,
since even ornithologists have realized that there are more than
two, the old error being due to the seafarer's notion that
individual man-o'-war birds regularly cross thousands of miles

of open ocean. We now know, on the contrary, that these birds are bound by firm homing ties to the stations where they roost and nest. A careful check of observations from all parts of the deep fails to substantiate the presence of any man-o'-war bird farther than about 200 miles from an island or continent. Broad reaches of ocean, however, are spangled with islets. The traveler in the South Sea, who sights the birds within a circle of unbroken watery horizon, would do well to consult his position on the chart before concluding that the palms of some forgotten atoll may not lie within eye-range from the lofty level of the man-o'-war. "Thou art all wings!" cried Walt Whitman, correctly. But since he next penned exultant lines about this glorious sea fowl's gyrations through spaces and realms of air—

"At dusk that look'st on Senegal, at morn America,"

it is unhappily necessary to point out that the only transoceanic flight really involved was a poetic one!

There are, in fact, five species of man-o'-war birds, ranging in size from creatures of 60-inch span to others that stretch a full eight feet from tip to tip of the wings. A single species may inhabit a whole ocean, or more, as in the case of our own Florida bird, which has representatives as far apart as West Africa and the Galápagos Islands. But comparison of museum specimens reveals that the birds from these several localities are not quite the same; rather, they prove to be subspecies or geographic races which, as a result of long isolation, have come to differ more or less one from another. Such change is a familiar expression of evolution. The Cape Verde Island man-o'-war of the eastern Atlantic, for example, is one race; the Caribbean bird, occurring from the southern United States to Brazil and Peru, another; the bird at the Galápagos Islands, which lie in the Pacific within 600 miles of South America, is still a third. Contrary to many published reports, the last has never yet been captured anywhere away from the immediate vicinity of its own islands, a fact easy to determine because it happens to be the largest man-o'-war bird in the world. Incidentally, a race of a second and smaller species has also reached and occupied the Galápagos, but from a different direction, namely, that of the Polynesian isles to westward. Thus two kinds, one of Atlantic and one of Pacific source, now dwell side by side at "World's End" without actually mingling. Their nesting territories seem to be mutually exclusive as to colonies if not also as to islands within the Galápagos group.

In the steps of the process that is sometimes called "speciation" we discern further evidence of the sedentary disposition of a bird once supposed to wander far and wide at will. If the latter were true, continual inbreeding would prevent the segregation of distinct island strains just as surely as unfenced Plymouth rocks mix their blood with the Rhode Island reds of an adjacent farm.

How then have the world oceans become peopled with a dozen or more species and subspecies of man-o'-war birds? Here the power of survival with which their mighty wings endow them suggests an answer. Neither they nor any other flying creature can fight the full strength of a tropical hurricane, but they, more than other sea birds, are often able to ride it out and with good fortune to be carried in safety to a new insular home. Following a September "twister," a man-o'-war bird has been taken in Nova Scotia, as far from its point of origin as many a remote island in the sea. By similar means, we may assume, successful colonies have been founded during long ages, and each time the home-clinging instinct has reasserted its isolating and hence creative sway.

It would be rash to assert that the relative distinctness of a man-o'-war bird population is certainly correlated with the time that has elapsed since the Adam—or rather the Eve—of the settlement first arrived from somewhere else. We know, nevertheless, that wherever inter-island distances are slight

and conditions for distribution favorable, birds of a single race
inhabit scores or hundreds of islets, as in the West Indies and
among the far-flung archipelagoes of the Pacific. On the other
hand, the tiny and lonely volcanic peak of Ascension in the
South Atlantic, 700 miles from the nearest island and farther
from any continent, is the sole home on earth of a man-o'-
war bird that has peculiarities not shared by any other. It
would be idle to speculate as to how many eons the members
of this tribe have reveled in uncontaminated aloofness.

It is a truism that many closely related birds differ much
more from each other in manner of life than in appearance.
Among man-o'-war birds the opposite is so. All seem to be alike
in structure and in habits; there is no equivalent example of
basal uniformity, indeed, in any equally large group of sea
birds. The specific distinctions between them relate almost
wholly to size and to pattern of plumage.

The amazing bodily proportions that give a full-grown
man-o'-war bird its undisputed superiority over all rivals make
sense only when considered from a physiological point of view.
They are nothing more nor less than products of unbalanced
growth, determined by the bearers of heredity in ancestral
germ cells and by internal secretions of glands that carry out
the foreordained architectural plan. For example, the naked
chick just out of the egg is hardly a man-o'-war bird at all.
Rather, it is a mere "bird," and an extremely ugly one at that,
with a stubby bill, *legs actually larger than its wings,* and
such a close resemblance to the young of its relatives, the pelicans, cormorants and boobies, that an interchange of nestlings
might fool even the parents. But the nondescript baby man-o'-
war has no sooner shaken off its shell than the biological dif-
ferential comes into play. The beak begins to lengthen and to
form a sharp hook; the legs grow very slowly and soon not at
all, while the bones of the wing rapidly double and redouble
their length. By the time the fledgling is ready to leave the
nest, a structural freak has been fashioned. The upper wing

bone has become three and a half times as long as the thigh bone and fifteen times as heavy, the middle wing bones more than four times the length of the shin bone. The ultimate result is a highly specialized flying machine, with feet barely large enough to grasp a perch, but with wings a yard in length, each furnished with 25 per cent more flight feathers and 40 per cent more area than those of a gull or other sea bird having the same bulk of body.

Power, strength and rigidity are abundantly supplied to match the vast planes. The great breast muscles that work them comprise nearly one-fourth the weight of the whole bird. The plumage alone, which includes flight feathers seventeen inches or more in length, makes up another quarter of the weight. The long, forked, scissors-like tail, highly important in the man-o'-war's aerial evolutions, is regulated by seven pairs of muscles attached to the spine, and its quills are firmly imbedded in a massive fibrous cushion. The skeleton is marvelously strong. The wishbone, unlike that of any other bird, is welded to the keel of the breastbone and to the two lateral stanchions of the shoulder-girdle, making a peerless frame for the attachment of the muscle-motor and for articulating the crankshafts of the wings. A typical female of the Caribbean race that I recently handled in the flesh gave figures startlingly disproportionate when compared with any other avian standard. Its total weight was 2 pounds 2½ ounces; its wing spread 89 inches; the whole imposing structure of the bird depended upon a skeleton which weighed, when dried, about one-quarter of a pound.

Our fledgling man-o'-war, therefore, begins its free life as an instinctive master of the light tropical atmosphere and an exponent of the effortless flight in which it excels every other bird. An albatross is impressive chiefly when the breeze is brisk; most smaller birds accomplish their spectacular feats by a rapid beating of the wings and high consumption of muscular energy; but the man-o'-war has the appearance of *floating* in air. He is the supreme model sailplane; when man has solved his secrets, motors and fuel will be auxiliaries rather than necessities of long-distance aviation. Such reflections are almost trite to the modern navigator who approaches an island anchorage with a canopy of man-o'-war birds above his topmasts. At such times the birds are likely to show a curious interest in snipping at the pennon, a trait recalled by Herman Melville in the closing passages of *Moby Dick*. As the *Pequod* sank to her doom, "a sky-hawk tauntingly . . . followed the main-truck downward from its natural home among the stars, pecking at the flag."

But, although the man-o'-war bird views the ocean all its days, it is meticulous to shun contact with its surface, because in the water this perfect glider is even worse off than when grounded. Once down, indeed, it is a helpless, floundering monstrosity, incapable either of making headway with its puny feet or of lifting itself back into the security of the air. Worst of all, its plumage quickly becomes water-logged because the oil-gland above its tail is a minute, atrophied affair, totally insufficient for the water-proofing purpose that this organ fulfills for all other sea fowl.

It is not unlikely that man-o'-war birds occasionally spend the night aloft during their longer wanderings from home. There is a persistent tradition among seamen that they sleep on the wing, but nobody has proved it. More often, at any rate, they sail back to familiar roosts and balance on their little feet from sunset until dawn. As night deepens, they become extraordinarily slumberous, or almost stupefied, so that to capture them is then an easy matter. Seventeenth-century accounts from the French West Indies tell of organized nocturnal raids by colonists and negroes, in which hundreds of man-o'-war birds were plucked from the branches and slaughtered for their fat, which was regarded as a sovereign remedy for rheumatic twinges, dropsy, and paralysis!

In the hands of less bloodthirsty captors, man-o'-war birds

are easily tamed and soon seem content to sit on a cross-bar and wait for fish to be tossed to them. Why not? No doubt they assume that they have subjugated an extraordinarily large, docile, and effective kind of booby! Such ready adaptability to a new role explains why they could be employed as "carrier pigeons" by the Polynesians. Among the Samoan Islands and elsewhere in the Pacific, it was customary to erect perches outside human dwellings and to feed the admired man-o'-war birds as they rested. When their excursions led them to other islands roundabout, they were quick to drop in at similar free-lunch counters. Thus, after the Christianization of Samoa, the missionaries found an ocean postal service awaiting their use, with written messages taking the place of the shell fishhooks and other small objects of olden time. Such post was not necessarily swift, but it was reasonably sure. One letter, placed in a reed cylinder and attached to the wing of a man-o'-war bird on a Friday, was delivered at an island 62 miles away on the following Sunday.

THE PARASOL ANT ✻ *It grows mushrooms in its maze-like underground home* ✻ BY V. WOLFGANG VON HAGEN.

IT WAS my misfortune to become intimately acquainted with the Parasol Ant during my expedition to the Mosquito Shore in Honduras. I planted a small garden in the jungle, a laborious affair that meant the felling of trees and the tearing up of lianas and other jungle creepers; but I was rewarded by uncovering a wide expanse of rich black loam which, with the alacrity of growth in the tropics, augured well for a rapidly yielding garden.

My Indian servants, dusky, kinky-haired Miskito men, lamented all this work. It was useless, quoth a toothless elder, to plant anything but bananas or manioc, as the *Wiwis* were sure to cut off all the leaves. Without the slightest encouragement, the Miskito Indians would launch forth on the tales of the ravages of the *Wiwi Laca*, but unswayed by the illustrations, like Pangloss I could only remark that all this was very well but let us cultivate our garden.

In two weeks the carrots, the cabbages, the turnips were doing well. The carrots had unfurled their fernlike tops, the cabbages grew as if by magic. From our small palm-thatched house my wife and I cast admiring eyes over our jungle garden. Our mind called forth dishes of steaming vegetables to replace dehydrated greens and the inevitable beans and yucca. Even the toothless Miskito elder came by and admitted that white man's energy had overcome the lethargy of the Indian. Then the catastrophe fell upon us.

We arose one morning and found our garden defoliated: every cabbage leaf was stripped, the naked stem was the only thing above the ground. Of the carrots nothing was seen. In

the center of the garden, rising a foot in height, was a conical
peak of earth, and about it were dry bits of earth, freshly
excavated. Into a hole in the mound, ants, moving in quick-
ened step, were carrying bits of our cabbage, tops of the carrots, the beans—in fact, our entire garden was going down
that hole. I could see the grinning face of the toothless Miskito
Indian. *The Wiwis had come.* As it was too near the rainy
season to begin another garden, I made no attempt to rid
myself of the ants, and we turned perforce to our dehydrated
vegetables, beans, and yucca for the duration of our collecting
trip on the Mosquito Coast.

Since we had the Parasol Ant with us,[1] and as I had prom-
ised Dr. Julian Huxley to obtain a colony for the Insect Vivarium of the London Zoo, I began the observations preparatory
to securing a group. To prepare a colony of these ants for a
long journey is not so simple as placing them in a box with
their larvae, food, and a moistened sponge. The Parasol Ant is
a vegetarian, a horticulturist, in short, a grower of mushrooms,
and more intimate details about its habits had to be known
before a nest could be transported.

The Parasol Ants, however, are the least difficult of organisms to observe. Night or day they can be seen moving from
their nests along one main "highway"—a hardened path three
inches wide, trampled bare by the ceaseless movement of millions of ants. Moving over this path which they have doubtless
cleaned of grass, come the rushing, hurrying legions of the
Leaf Cutters. The broad-headed workers are maroon-colored,
a half-inch in length, and are accompanied by other poly-
morphic workers somewhat smaller. It is an industrious group.
The incoming ants with their waving leaf banners collide with
the legions of the outgoing ants. When the ants run into each
other, there may be a brief pause while the ant with the leaf
and the ant in search of one tap each other with their antennae.

[1] It is sometimes called the Umbrella Ant, though it does not work in the
rain.

The "highway" runs some distance from the nest and loses itself in the jungle verdure, for from that point on the ants take themselves to the vegetation for their cuttings. I followed a contingent of the ants to a low-lying, broad-leafed Heliconia (a not distant relative of the plantain), and watched them mount the stems and join their fellows wandering on the wide surface of the leaf. That this plant pleased the Leaf Cutters was evident, for some of the stems of the Heliconia were standing bare and bald, devoid of leaf. One leaf, recently unfurled and moist from its compact growth, was filled with ants rushing excitedly about it, colliding with one another, making a rapid play over the body with the antennae, then hurrying away again to tap the edge of the leaf. Some of the ants were already cutting, and I bent closer with a magnifying glass to watch the performance, being careful to shield my breath from them. Holding by four of its legs to the leaf, a worker would lean forward to the edge and start to cut by opening and closing its mandibles. The jaws are heavily dentated and move across one another, functioning like shears. The cutting is always done in a quarter circle, arc-like. When the ant has cut a piece of leaf somewhat larger than itself, it grasps one edge as it makes the last cut through the fibers. Bracing itself, it pulls backward and, gripping the leaf anew, raises it over its head and moves toward the ground. Likely as not at this stage will appear another ant, which eagerly (and one might almost be tempted to say enthusiastically) taps the ant and its leaf with its antennae and then lays hold of the leaf with its own mandibles. This is, of course, not at all sporting, and for some while there is a tug-of-war between the two, with the owner usually winning by its spirited tenacity.

Again on the ant highway, the worker with its Heliconia "flag" moves along with its fellows to the nest. In the cool of the morning, with the sunlight piercing through the heavy vegetation, one can make out an unending stream of Leaf

Cutters. From a distance, with the ant barely seen under its burden, it appears as if a breeze were ruffling the bits of jungle undergrowth. On the ground the workers returning with their burdens are met by other minuscule inhabitants of the ant nest, tiny workers one-fourth the size of the larger workers. These do not cut or carry leaves, but can always be seen hurrying along the path. One will mount the back of the worker and, climbing on top of the leaf, hold to this leafy perch on its way to the nest.

The path leads to the central entrance; and without letting go of the leaf, the worker descends. What happens to the leaves? My Miskito Indian insisted that the *Wiwis* take the leaf below and feed it to a larger ant, which, when it grows large enough, comes from the nest and makes off into the forest where it becomes a wild pig. Bates, the English naturalist, when on the Amazon, gave his studied opinion. The leaves he said were brought below to carpet the nests, and others were placed about the entrances to stop the water from running into the hole during the torrential rains. Later, Belt in Nicaragua, came to the conclusion that the best way of finding out what they did with the leaves was to open the nest and see for oneself. What he found was startling enough.

The leaves were used as fertilizer for large fungus gardens which the Parasol Ants grow in their subterranean chambers deep in the earth. He insisted the ants live exclusively on this fungus, and the suggested symbiosis between plant and insect was of such interest that Alfred Moeller in Brazil gave himself over to the matter and communicated some of his observations to Darwin. The fungus, Moeller found, is actually an artificial culture of a *Rhozites gongylophora,* a whitish moldlike fungus mycelium, which does not develop into large mushrooms because of some action performed on the heads of the mycelium by the ants. He further proved Belt's theory that the ants live exclusively on the fungus, the ants providing the

fungus with the substratum for its growth and the mycelium
in turn repaying its part of the symbiotic bargain by growing
luxuriantly in the chambers made for it.

This then, became our problem: if the ants live only on the
fungus and must have leaves to fertilize it, how could I construct such a nest and transport the ants in a three-months'
journey to London. To see more of this organism, I also opened
the nest. Now, this is not a simple task. These ants build immense nests, some of which have been estimated to spread
over 100 cubic meters of earth. The excavated mounds tower
to as much as five feet above the earth, and the subterranean
regions are as deep as nine feet.

We began our excavation fifteen feet from the central
cone—on the outside edge of the nest. We began a broad
trench into the mound; and by keeping up a relay of Indians, I
had the trench fairly well into the center of the mound in the
first hour. By this time we had run into trouble, for our digging had disturbed yet another type of Parasol Ant, the soldier:
and the more we dug into the center, the more spirited became the defense. We had reached the center when suddenly
one of the Indians gave a blood-curdling shriek and made for
the jungle. We stood aghast watching him, and then the other
Indians screamed and began beating about them. The soldiers
had called the reserves and they had come in hordes and were
now crawling over us, biting and drawing blood. These soldiers are twice the size of the worker, about an inch in length,
with large heart-shaped heads and immense mandibles. Once
they bit they held on so tightly that the only way to remove
them was to crush the whole ant.

Indians, taking full advantage of this tenacity, use the soldier ant to suture wounds. When one has cut his arm, he holds
the cut together, takes a live ant by the back and places it near
the wound. The soldier ant bites deep, clamping the two edges
of the skin together as in a vise. The Indian then takes another
ant and performs the same operation near the first and so on

down the length of the wound. The next step is merely to wring their necks and snap off the body from the head. The ant will not relax its hold even though decapitated; and if it were aseptic, this method could replace catgut sutures in emergency.

The excavating was now difficult, owing to the interruption occasioned by beating off the soldier ants, so I had recourse to a modern turn: I sent one of the Indians after my Flit-gun. Filled with insecticide, this proved just the right thing. Every few minutes we would spray each other and kill or stun the soldier ants on our clothes, until eventually we were so permeated with the fluid that the soldier ants kept from us.

In the center of the nest we uncovered the large spongy masses of fungus. They were as large as cauliflower heads, of a grayish color, and so flocculent that, like soap bubbles, they collapsed with pressure. The fungus grew from the bottom of the rounded mud cell: and housed within the interior of it were eggs, nymphs, soldiers, small and large golden-winged alates. As soon as we broke into the fungus garden, the alates made quickly for the dark recesses of the fungus, while the broad-headed soldiers moved toward us, making in all their myriads a curious rustling sound. On one side of the cell was an entrance, and unmindful of the catastrophe that descended on their fungus garden, the workers with their leaf banners continued to pour through it into the nest. Atta is ultramethodical; repeated catastrophes have to occur before it takes cognizance of them; so, despite the hurried antennae-tapping of the ants in flight, the workers continued to come with their burdens. They dropped these on the floor of the garden, reflectingly tapped the fungus with their antennae, and left through the same entrance without so much as being disturbed by the fact that their gardens were in danger. When matters quieted down in the opened nest, other workers, the Lilliputians of the Parasol Ant world, confined wholly to the fungus crypts, swarmed over the freshly gathered leaves. Under the

magnifying glass I could see their small mandibles crushing
the leaf into minute pellets, which they carried into the mass
of fungus and buried in the crannies. This then was the ultimate end of the leaf—fertilizer for these gardens.

Each fungus garden is a complete world in itself. It receives its quota of eggs from the central reproductive chamber,
which is larger than the rest and usually found below the other
cells. In this nest we counted 40 distinct cells of irregular sizes,
round and spheroid, covering an immense stretch of ground.
The many thousands of workers composing this colony had
been produced from eggs laid by a few gravid females. Most
good-sized ant colonies contain more than a single queen, but
the number of these fecundated egg-laying individuals is
never large. As quickly as the eggs are laid, the workers carry
them off to the cells and place them in the warm confines of
the mycelium gardens. The egg hatches, and through its larval
growth it is tended by the workers. Each cell within this formic
republic is complete within itself yet held together by that
obese matriarch below, which produces the new life for the
colony.

Had M. Fourier, the French mathematician who conceived the ideal co-operative social unit known as the phalanastery, wished an example, he could have found no clearer one in
nature than the community of the Parasol Ant. For his Utopia,
M. Fourier suggested that mankind be segregated into units
of 2000 occupying a single dwelling and each providing
itself with its own amusements and necessities. Each individual of the phalanastery would be permitted to pursue whatever employment he was best fitted for by natural aptitude.
There were to be no salaries; but each was to receive an ample
minimum and a share of the surplus.

Fourier's system did not work, but the caste system of the
Parasol Ant permits it to exercise its specialized aptitudes
in this communal way of life. Each member is limited from

performing a task other than that which its own physiology will permit.

To regulate its community, the Parasol Ant has a common dumping ground where the used, dried leaf-fertilizer is disposed of along with the dead ants. Emerging from all of the fungus chambers, tunnels lead to this dump, where ceaselessly the workers bring the refuse and drop it, as a miner might dispose of the waste of a mine. Raking among the debris, I uncovered numerous large Staphylinid beetles feeding on the dead exo-skeletons of the ants. Curiously shaped beetles, generally apterous, or "wingless," they live on friendly terms with the ants and can with impunity wander among the galleries and fungus gardens. As the beetles have the same nest odor as the Parasol Ant and as they exude from the base of their anal extremities a delectable liquor which the ants lap up avidly, the Staphylinid beetles have become part of the formic republic. The beetles are lacking in decorum, however, for instead of confining themselves strictly to a coprophagous diet they plunder the live young larvae of the nest, and if unchecked one might believe that they could seriously undermine the ant colony.

With the beginning of the rainy season, the winged species take to the air to mate and then to create new colonies. For some days before the nuptial flight there is an animated tenseness within the formicary. Then one day when the rain pours down in torrents, the winged species feel the time has come and emerge into the open. The alates are twice as large as the soldiers, with great golden membraned wings. One can readily distinguish between the male and female, for the male is smaller but has larger eyes than the female. As the whole system is based on the principle of matriarchy, the female has a larger body, with a greatly developed thorax to propel the enormous wings. These winged species, making their exit from the subterranean chambers, poise for an instant and then soar into the air to become victims of this great genital frenzy. The males follow the females, and fecundation takes place, usually in the air. The female is pursued by many males, one of whom she selects as a mate before they fall to earth, locked in a golden cloud to be dispersed by the death of the males. Poor males of the insect cosmos, they are only casual intruders in a purely feminine world.

The fertilized female then seeks and digs out a place in the earth, where she breaks off her wings. For this time at least, she loses the blue-blooded prerogatives of a queen and performs all the menial tasks of the workers. It is at this stage that the colony is an amazing illustration of the directive instinct of the insects. Dr. Carlos Bruch found that just before the females leave the nest for the nuptial flight they feed heavily on the fungus. The threadlike hyphae of the fungus as well as other particles of the substratum become packed in the "infrabuccal pocket" and form a large pellet. This the female retains until she has made her little cell underneath the ground, whereupon she regurgitates the hyphae pellet onto the floor of the chamber. Caring for her garden and using her feces for the manure to insure its rapid growth, the Queen meanwhile is busily laying her first eggs. As soon as the workers mature, they take over the duties imposed upon them, and the Queen becomes less active as she grows older. Finally she abandons forever any tasks connected with the operation of the colony and becomes virtually an egg-laying machine.

The Parasol Ants are a potential force antagonistic to civilization, if it be true that civilization is based on agriculture. Were it not for the fact that the swarming sexual reproductive forms are set on by reptile, bird, and man, their numbers would overwhelm the vegetation. At the time of the swarm, Indians of the Amazon construct miniature dirigible-shaped baskets, which they hold over the exits of the nests so that the flying insects fall into them. Birds perch in near-by trees to fly down and eat them as they emerge, among them the resplendent trogon, which takes them on the wing; and immense frogs merely sit near the nest and with their flat, mucus-covered tongues swallow them as fast as the winged ants appear. So the supernumeraries of the Parasol Ants serve man again, for almost all the Indians of the Amazon as well as those on the Mosquito Coast have developed a taste for them. The workers and soldiers have sharp spines coming from the thorax and the top of their heads. Generally these castes are avoided by birds, but the winged castes have no such spikes; and seeing my Miskito Indian devouring them, I decided that I, too, would try this formic delicacy. All Indians have names for this ant and all eat it, from the head-hunting Jivaros, who call it *uku* and eat it raw, to the Jicaques of Central America who like their *ara* cooked. My Miskito Indians would pull off the heads, legs, and wings, and toast them in a sort of flat *cumal*; and I must own that the flavor was not bad, somewhat resembling crisped bacon. For the day at least, we all became insatiable Molochs eating the ants as fast as the little children brought them to us; but, eventually wearying of the pungent oily taste, I gave the signal that I, for one, had had enough of this repast.

On the way back to our camp, laden with the nest for the London Zoo, filled as it was with the crumply fungus and all the ant-forms, we found that the Parasol Ants, now that the nuptial flight had ended, had taken up their interrupted tasks and were again cutting and carrying their leaves along the ant-highways through the jungle to their nests, beginning yet another yearly cycle.

Owing to the fact that our traveling formicary was held up in transit and lay three weeks on a dock, it did not reach London successfully. Such are the disappointments when one tries to move a "universe." But a new attempt will be made in the near future.

🕮 THE CURIOUS SEA HORSE 🕮 *One of the oddest fishes in the sea* 🕮 BY RENÉ THÉVENIN.

IT IS easy to understand how a type of fishes so singular in appearance as the *Hippocampi* or sea horses should formerly have been thought of as a group far apart from all others.

The French scientist, Georges Cuvier, created for them (and for their cousins the *Syngnathi* or sea needles) the order of Lophobranchiata. As the name implies, the distinction depended upon the gills, which in the sea horse grow in the form of tufts instead of in comblike formation as in most other fishes.

Today it is known that this characteristic of the respiratory system is also found in other fishes in various stages of development. Likewise, the armor of the sea horse, which protects its body and which replaces the scales, is not absolutely unique. But in spite of these later discoveries which minimized somewhat their strangeness, the *Hippocampi* still deserve special interest because of their unusual appearance and their habits.

Sea horses are primarily inhabitants of the warmer seas, though a few representatives may be found in comparatively cold waters. In Europe, where we studied them especially, they occur as far north as in the Channel. But they begin to be rare in these latitudes, whereas they are very common in the Mediterranean Sea.

The most abundant varieties do not grow larger than about two inches, but the tropical forms sometimes attain much greater size. In the Australian Seas and also near Japan large specimens occur. The largest are possibly two feet in length.

Their appearance also varies, but in general they justify fully the popular name "sea horse." The head of these fishes closely resembles that of a horse, or, even more exactly, the "knight" in the game of chess. Their skin shows no scales but instead a "skin-skeleton," similar to that of the insects. The plates that form this skin-skeleton are connected with each other in rings that give the body of the animal the shape of an irregular polyhedron. One can count 50-odd such rings from the neck to the lower end of the body. The shields that ride on the back of the fish like the tiles of a roof produce a crest on the head, the neck, and the back. In certain varieties, especially those of the warm seas, these appendages are elongated, overgrown, and branched in the most extraordinary fashion, and seemingly for camouflage resemble the marine plants among which the creatures live.

One of the peculiarities of this family is that, unlike all other fishes, its members swim in an upright position. And the tail is not used for propelling the animal at all but only for gripping a more or less solid support around which it curves itself like a spiral. This support is usually a plant of some sort, but any other object might serve the same purpose. It is easy, in fact, to have a sea horse clinging to one's finger in an aquarium. To bring this about, it is only necessary to touch its caudal extremity gently. One notices in this instant how much gripping power the little tail of the fish has; it could be compared to that of a small child's hand. The sea horse is the only fish aside from the closely related Nerophis that has a prehensile tail. Nerophis, of which at least two species are known in Europe only, belongs to the same family as the sea horse.

The tail is restricted to this use and does not serve as a fin. The anal fin is also reduced to the simplest form and apparently no longer has any function. The fins that are normally found in pairs on the bodies of fishes are represented only by those farthest forward, namely, the pectoral fins, which are placed just behind the gills. They are used to maintain the vertical position and the equilibrium of the body in the water. The only really active fin is the dorsal fin, which oscillates in a rapid, rhythmic manner, reminding one almost of a propeller.

The sea horse does not swim much. Hooked to a bunch of seaweed, it remains motionless in its vertical position. If it does not discard its support, it has no exercise at all.

The structure of the head is extraordinary, too. It ends with an elongated snout, which opens and closes with a rapid movement. One can distinctly hear the faint smacking sound it makes when the sea horse snaps at its prey.

All these characteristics may easily be observed in an aquarium, where sea horses can be kept alive without any difficulty. This at least applies to our native (French) varieties, especially *Hippocampus antiquorum*, which is the variety I am describing.

This animal certainly accustoms itself easily to changes in temperature, as well as to changes in the salt content of the water—even to a change of diet. Its food consists, in captivity, of little shrimps, worms, and even small pieces of meat, which the sea horse catches by a very quick movement of its head the instant they come near its mouth. It is in this moment that one can hear—when listening carefully—the sound produced by the opening of the mouth. The prey is swallowed quickly without being chewed.

In the act of catching its prey the animal is greatly aided by the mobility of its eyes. They are placed on the sides of the head and are independent of each other. Their way of working reminds one of the eyes of the chameleon. The eyes of the sea horse appear to sense very slight changes of form and illumination.

Light apparently has also an important influence on the general coloration of the body. The color varies not only with the species but also with the surroundings in which the specimens are found. The most common color is a dark gray, almost black. But reddish, greenish, and silverish colors are also found; and quite often the body shows very brilliant spots.

Male specimens sometimes show the dorsal fin rimmed with yellow; the coloration of the females is less pronounced.

When these dark colors turn to a greenish-yellow or even to white, it is a sign of bad health, and the animal usually dies very soon afterward. At the same time, the sea horse abandons its vertical position and begins to swim on its side. Sometimes bleedings occur, accompanied by losses of skin, which may lead to the loss of parts of the tail. Most frequently all these signs of bad health do not show before it is too late to help.

When the sea horse descends, it curves its neck and rolls its tail in. When it wants to float upward, it straightens itself out almost completely. It can also creep on the bottom by little movements of the body and tail.

The breathing is done, as has already been stated, by means of pufflike gills. In the moment when the water is inhaled, the tongue bones or hyoid bones are erected and poke out the skin from the inside, producing the semblance of little horns.

The rigidity of the skin-skeleton makes it exceedingly easy to preserve the bodies of sea horses. The mummified little forms are picked up on the shores of the Mediterranean by the children—especially in Naples—and constitute the stock of a minor trade, or, more exactly, an excuse for begging.

But the most interesting thing to observe in sea horses is their manner of reproduction and their way of caring for the young.

The adult female carries about two hundred eggs. When the time has come for mating, the male and female approach each other and begin to make movements which may be compared to a dance.

The male is equipped with a ventral pocket or pouch which extends from the twelfth to the eighteenth ring and has its place underneath the pelvic bone. To be exact, there are two pockets in the skin, right and left, which join in the middle in the adult, leaving only a small slotlike opening.

The female inserts her cloacal appendix into this slot and projects her eggs into the male pouch; while passing the slot they become fecundated. This brings to a conclusion the duties of the mother, and thenceforth the father performs the role of a mother—a unique reversal of the usual habits.

When the pouch of the male sea horse is not occupied, it is lined with conjunctive tissue, which is only slightly wrinkled. But from the moment that the eggs are deposited, a considerable change takes place. The tissue begins to swell and to grow, it becomes spongelike, and the capillary blood vessels enlarge and multiply. In short, placentation is occurring. Interesting speculation surrounds the question as to how the male may have developed this complex function.

Soon after the eggs have entered the pouch, each one produces a localized excitation; little holes form, the whole tissue takes on the appearance of a quadrangular network, and each compartment engulfs one egg. In addition, a wall begins to grow from the bottom of the pouch and approaches the seam of the outer skin of the pouch so that it is divided into two parts. Thus two additional surfaces are created, which give the remainder of the eggs a chance to secure a place on the pseudo-placental tissue. Those that do not succeed in finding a place where they can develop degenerate.

The successful eggs start to develop at once, and as they grow they embrace more and more tissue.

The shell, or rather the skin of each egg splits open inside the pocket, but the embryo is not yet expelled. It rests in the pseudo-placental tissue and remains in this position usually until its yolk is used up almost entirely. During this time, it has the curved position of many embryos and does not straighten itself out until it is finally projected into the water.

Sometimes it happens, however, that a few embryos are expelled while still in possession of a fairly large yolk sac. It is to be noted that these are handicapped in the struggle for existence. The young ones best equipped to meet the dangers of life are those that have freed themselves completely from the natural reserves of the embryonic stage. These also swim in the vertical position at once, the position customary for the sea horses. They even show the adult tilt of the head at once.

Further proof that the connection between the young ones and the father is a very close one can be observed in the fact that the male suffers considerable difficulty in the act of expulsion. He can be seen writhing on the soil, rubbing his body and struggling energetically. At the same time, his eyes are wide open and move convulsively in the rhythm of breathing. Finally, with considerable force the male ejects its burden of young sea horses, along with the residue of the eggs, pieces of tissue, and many bubbles of gas.

The pouch does not empty all at once. There are several expulsions, which may extend over a number of days in the form of consecutive spasms. Even when the pouch is finally empty, the contractions continue for a time, slowly becoming less violent. Finally the pouch is deflated, and its slot, wide open during the expulsion, closes again. The tissue in the pouch returns to normal, and the network of blood vessels becomes more ample.

A few accidents may happen during this period. The pouch may close over a comparatively large amount of gases not ejected together with the embryos. These gases, of course, disturb the buoyancy of the animal. In the aquarium it is easy to catch the specimen and to insert a narrow tube or cannula into the pouch and allow the gas to escape, pressing gently against the sides of the body to expel it.

After the young sea horses can no longer draw from their father or their reserves of yolk, they have to seek their nourishment independently by the normal means. Their appearance at this time still varies even with specimens of the same variety, according to the conditions of their birth. Those that are "born" prematurely still carry the burden of their vitelline sac, swimming awkwardly in a horizontal position. In spite of the yolk sac, which tends to drag them down to the bottom, they swim near the surface, probably because their still highly developed swim-bladder keeps them afloat.

Their eyes are still very large and remind the observer of the eyes of the embryos still in the egg. On the other hand, the snout is very short and so to speak flattened out over the face. The face looks vaguely like that of a Pekinese dog. The body is still more or less transparent, and one can see the tiny heart beating. But soon the first spots of pigmentation begin to appear here and there, in a strange pattern. Slowly the distribution of these spots becomes more regular, and they begin to look like stars. The blots unite and cover the whole surface of the body, which becomes opaque and takes on the coloration of the adult.

Though normally it should occur at the time of birth, the snout sometimes does not protrude until an advance date. But finally the head assumes the adult position at right angles to the body and the animal begins to swim in the vertical position. At the same time, the little animal descends deeper into the water and begins to look for a water plant as a support. Quite often, the young ones, misled by limited experience, try to attach themselves to non-solid objects such as air bubbles that come from the plants or float on the surface of the water.

The sexual characteristics do not appear before several months have elapsed. Not before that time can the forming of the male pouch and the female appendix be observed. Generally speaking, the animal is not ripe for reproduction before the following year. In our European climate, the couples begin to unite in spring, and the events we have described take place sometime in the summer, according to circumstances. The expulsion of the young ones takes place 40 to 50 days after fecundation.

These are the curious life habits of the sea horse—life habits that have been known to naturalists for hardly a century. To be sure, the incubation pouch was long ago mentioned by classical authors, but quite naturally it was attributed by them to the female, and careful observation by scientists was necessary to reveal that the opposite condition existed.

The final achievement in elucidating the life habits of the sea horse should perhaps be accredited to Monsieur Jean Painlevé, for it was his skillful studies with the motion picture camera that made it possible for the man in the street to observe and understand them.

The first person to observe the intertwining of sea horses in the act of transferring the eggs was probably Dufosse, a Frenchman, in 1854. He published his description in 1874; and in the same year Fanzago, in the zoological station in Naples, observed the same process. In 1867, Lockwood, an American, saw the delivery of the young.

Huot, another Frenchman, published a paper in 1902 in which he showed sections through the egg pouch. He showed that the epithelium makes nests surrounding each egg and that the network of blood vessels supplies nourishment to the eggs by osmosis. Cohn extended and confirmed Huot's observation.

≈ THE UNBIRDLIKE KIWI ≈ *Even some scientists insisted, "There ain't no sech animal"* ≈ BY VION AND BERNARD SCHRAM.

AT A CRUCIAL point in the Pacific war, supplies for the New Zealand troops stationed on New Caledonia failed to arrive on schedule. Familiar with military mix-ups, the supply sergeant began a canvass of other allied depots.

He inquired at the American base, "Are the Kiwi supplies here?"

The bewildered Yank in charge scratched his head and asked, "*Whose* supplies?"

Then, after a moment's thought, enlightenment dawned.

"Oh, you mean those boxes with the picture of a long-nosed, flat-bottomed duck marked K-one-W-one?"

The "flat-bottomed duck marked K-one-W-one" was none other than New Zealand's national emblem, a creature almost as out-of-date in modern times as a dinosaur, and the exclusive pride and joy of New Zealand, the only place in the world where kiwis are found.

Even ornithologists label the kiwi "the queerest and most unbirdlike of living birds." It resembles almost everything but what it actually is. Unable to fly, the kiwi's naked and useless wings are concealed beneath thick, hairlike feathers, so that its body looks more like a hedgehog's than a bird's. Its long beak, with a tuft of catlike whiskers at the base, gives its head the appearance of an anteater's. At first glance you might even think the skin was a mammal's rather than a bird's. It is tough and leathery enough to be made into gloves and moccasins.

Very few foreigners and not so very many New Zealanders have seen a kiwi. Because of its timid love of darkness and its habit of digging rabbit-style burrows for daylight nesting, the

214

kiwi was called "the hidden bird" by the Maoris, who thought it was under the special protection of Tane, god of the forest. However, this did not prevent these Polynesian hunters from tracking down kiwis for food and for their feathers, from which cloaks were made. Some of these early Maori cloaks, woven from native flax and kiwi feathers, are still in good condition though they were made as long as 200 years ago—a tribute to the durability of the kiwi's hairlike plumage.

The Maoris named the bird kiwi in imitation of its cry—a shrill whistle that sounds like *keeeee-wheee.*

Before the advent of the white man in New Zealand, kiwis abounded, despite large numbers slain by the Maoris. Fortunately, from a kiwi's point of view, New Zealand had no native mammals or reptiles to prey upon it, so that it was as safe from attack on the ground as in the air. Thus it was able to survive as a curious, earth-bound bird, with vestigial wings measuring hardly two inches in length.

The downfall of the kiwi resulted from the nostalgia of English pioneers who longed for their familiar sports. Soon after establishing themselves in New Zealand, the settlers introduced all manner of foreign birds and animals to provide themselves with good hunting quarry. But they made one grave mistake: they loosed English rabbits and hares upon the countryside. Living up to their reputation for fecundity, the rodents soon multiplied until they became pests, threatening farm crops and ruining gardens. So the settlers promptly brought in stoats and ferrets to control them. This step also proved a boomerang.

The weasels quickly discovered that the native New Zealand birds, made unwary by centuries of life without ground enemies, were easier prey than the rabbits. The kiwi, which had the added disadvantage of being unable to fly, was almost entirely at the mercy of the imported killers. In short order, the kiwis were so reduced in numbers that New Zealand bird lovers feared they were doomed to extinction.

Yet another menace came from an unexpected direction. In their enthusiasm for sports, the New Zealand pioneers introduced American and European trout into their streams and lakes. In their avid experimentation in quest of artificial flies with trout appeal, they decided, with the inexplicable logic of the fisherman, that the drab brown and gray feathers of the kiwi made lures irresistible to the fish. Consequently, they scoured the countryside with dogs and guns, slaughtering hundreds of kiwis for their plumage.

As a result of these onslaughts from all directions, kiwis became a curiosity instead of a commonplace bird in New Zealand.

By 1908, the kiwi had become so rare that a law was passed making it illegal for anyone to "take or kill" a kiwi without special government authorization. The law was weak and subject to widespread violation, so that in 1921 a new act was passed, which proclaimed the kiwi an "absolutely protected bird" and made it illegal for anyone to possess stuffed specimens, feathers, eggs, or Maori handicraft objects made with kiwi feathers, without permission from the Minister of Internal Affairs. The law also prohibited, on penalty of a $100 fine, the making of trout flies from kiwi feathers. A ban on exportation of the birds has been in effect since the 1908 law.

These laws, rigidly enforced by New Zealand's wildlife rangers, have helped to check the decline of the kiwi population, although the stoats and ferrets continue their raids. Conservation enforcement is difficult in any land. Dogs destroy large numbers, and vigilance for the welfare of the kiwi will continue to be necessary.

Ever since the initial word of its existence brought to Europe by early nineteenth century explorers, the kiwi has been the object of curiosity and incredulity. Zoologists expressed frank disbelief in the existence of this "ball of fur on two sticks." Even when Captain Barclay of the ship "Providence" brought a kiwi skin back to England in 1812, scientists imitated the farmer who, seeing a giraffe for the first time, stoutly maintained, "There ain't no sech animal." Later, when a live kiwi was presented to the London Zoological Garden, they were forced to admit that the fantastic bird actually existed.

Kiwis then became the rage among bird fanciers. Lord Rothschild collected a number of specimens for his private aviary. The Emperor of Austria and Hungary secured a pair for his personal zoo. Collectors and zoological gardens all over the world vied in procuring the weird birds.

All had the same experience. The nocturnal birds lived only a short time in captivity, and none produced young, even though one obliging kiwi in London sat on an infertile egg for 114 days before admitting defeat!

But the kiwi egg proved as great a curiosity as the ungainly bird itself. One species of kiwi weighs only five or six pounds at full maturity yet lays an egg weighing a pound or more— almost a quarter the size of the bird itself. So disproportionately large is the egg that just before it is laid, the overladen hen staggers under the weight like a drunken sailor in a gale. Even the ostrich, which may weigh as much as 250 pounds, lays eggs that are only slightly larger; and the domestic turkey, a much bigger fowl, lays an egg less than a third the size of the kiwi's.

It was only three years ago that the first kiwi chick was hatched in captivity, enabling scientists to report that the kiwi male is easily the most henpecked husband in the world.

The credit for this achievement goes to F. D. Robson, Curator of the Hawkes Bay Acclimatization Society's game farm near Napier, New Zealand. An expert in raising pheasants and trout for release in the Hawkes Bay area, Robson acquired— illegally, it may be added—his first kiwi some seventeen years ago. It was a fully grown, five-year-old cock that had been captured by pig hunters, who kept it secretly until it escaped. The frightened fugitive bird was found huddled in a Napier factory coal bin and was turned over to Robson. Curious to learn the habits of the rare creature, Robson ignored the law requiring him to report possession of the bird to the wildlife officials.

Robson kept his kiwi for six years, until he was fortunate enough to acquire a badly injured one-month-old chick that had been caught in a bush fire. He carefully nursed the chick, a hen, for five years until she reached maturity. She then started on an egg-laying spree that refuted all authorities who had previously claimed the kiwi could lay but one of its monumental eggs a year. Within a four-month period, Robson's hen laid four eggs—all of which, however, proved to be infertile.

By this time, word of his under-the-counter kiwis reached the ears of the authorities. Considerable controversy arose, with the influential Hawkes Bay Acclimatization Society taking Robson's part. At length, a special cabinet meeting handed down a decision that Robson could keep his pets in order to observe their breeding habits, on condition that he provide the Department of Internal Affairs with semiannual reports on his findings.

On September 19, 1945, Robson announced an event that held as much interest for New Zealanders as the Dionne quintuplets for the Canadians: the first kiwi was hatched in captivity! Unlike Papa Dionne, whose role had been all but ignored, Papa Kiwi came in for the lion's share of the credit.

For weeks, New Zealand newspapers printed almost daily reports on the progress of the setting, and editorials featured the brow-beaten male kiwi as the most notable victim of female emancipation.

As Robson describes the situation, "After Mama Kiwi laid the huge egg, she lost all interest. It was Papa Kiwi who made the nest and sat on the egg for 80 days until it was hatched. Sometimes he wouldn't leave the nest for a week, going without food; and at the end of the ordeal, he had lost two pounds in weight. He didn't look much bigger than the chick when it was hatched.

"While he was on the egg, he was so maternal he'd attack anyone who approached him, and the only time the hen came close was just before the egg was hatched. One day she came to the box in which the male was nesting and rapped on the outside with her beak. He replied by tapping on the box from inside. They must have been using some kind of Morse code, because she went away satisfied and took no further notice of the incubation."

Insult was added to injury for male vanity when the kiwi hen laid a second egg only 26 days after the first, just when the poor male had gotten well settled on it. As a consequence, the harassed husband had to extend his vigil to 100 days, at the end of which not one but two chicks had been hatched. Last season he had an even worse ordeal. Five eggs were laid over a period of six months, and the male bird sat continuously for 185 days.

News of the new arrivals traveled round the world among bird circles. In America, the tale of the kiwi chicks and the birds' gigantic eggs caught the eye of an enterprising poultry farmer. Without delay he wrote to Robson requesting all details, with an eye to crossing kiwis with his hens to produce larger eggs.

"When he heard that kiwis only lay a couple of eggs a year, he lost interest," Robson reports.

Since then Robson has been assailed with bids for the kiwis, which are really wards of the state in his custody. One American bird fancier has offered $1200 for a fertile kiwi egg and promised to arrange for its delivery to the States by air. More recently, an American tourist, a little the worse for a farewell shipboard party, landed in Auckland and demanded to know, "Where can I buy one of those kiwi birds?" Undismayed at the

news that kiwis were not for sale anywhere, he lurched down
the street, proclaiming, "I'd give $50 for one of these d----d
birds."

All such proposals, including a patriotic suggestion to present a pair of kiwis to Winston Churchill in appreciation for
his war services, have been politely rejected.

Wildlife officials point out, "The kiwi is not a bird that
adapts itself to exhibition. It is a night bird, accustomed to
sleeping during the daytime, just when people would want
to see it. Moreover, its food demands are such that it does not
appear to thrive on a strange diet. Therefore, no kiwis are being
released for zoos."

In reality, the Wellington Zoo has two kiwis on a basis of
dubious legality. Residents of the zoo for many years, the kiwis
roam the bush adjacent to the menagerie area. They are
caught on rare occasions for display to important visitors and
were penned for some months for the benefit of American
troops stationed in New Zealand during World War II.
When queried about the kiwis, the curator innocently lifts his
eyebrows and protests, "We have no kiwis in captivity. There
may be wild ones on the grounds, but we can't be responsible
for them."

However, the kiwis' presence is all too well known to the
zoo gardener. The birds have taken a fancy to his rose garden,
in the beds of which they probe nightly in quest of worms.
Lately, they have developed an unaccountable taste for rose-
bush shoots and, much to the gardener's dismay, have completely stripped the plot of young plants.

Robson is a whole-hearted sympathizer in regard to the
kiwis' "food demands." The baby kiwis at the game farm are
born weighing only six to ten ounces. During the first four
days of their life, they are too weak to support themselves on
their own legs, and Papa Kiwi, who by this time has had
enough trouble with them, doesn't bother to feed them. On the
sixth day, the chicks stalk out on their own and start boring

into the ground with their beaks in search of worms. For the first two weeks of their life, they lose weight. Then they commence to gain, and at the end of three months they each consume one and a half pounds of worms a day.

The daily worm diet for the chicks, with slightly less for the adults, keeps Robson hard at work. Although he stumbled across the expedient of "planting worms" by burying bits of meat from which maggots hatch, he still spends many hours engaged in worm digging.

"Do you know how many worms it takes to make a pound and a half?" he asks ruefully. "It takes 800."

His kiwi brood now numbers six—the original pair, three of their offspring, and "Pegleg Pete."

"Pegleg Pete" is a recent acquisition. Some months ago, he was caught in a possum trap, which broke his leg. The trapper turned the injured kiwi over to the conservator of game, who was forced to amputate the broken leg in order to save the bird's life. Then it was sent to Robson.

Robson has ingeniously devised a pegleg for the bird by whittling a hollow joint of bamboo to fit the stump and making it fast with a piece of rubber tubing. Today "Pete" hops around so agilely on his pegleg that he frequently eludes Robson when the curator seeks to catch him in the large enclosure housing the kiwis. Consequently, Robson sometimes has to resort to trickery. Sighting the bird, Robson will make a scratching noise on the ground to startle him. When the myopic kiwi charges blindly forward, Robson jumps to one side. The bird butts into the wire fence, and the curator captures him before he recovers his balance.

Robson has his own theory about why kiwis lost the power of flight. He bases it on the fact that the kiwi has very poor eyesight—with a range of vision limited to about two feet in daylight and six feet at night. He states that a bird so blind could never fly in the forest without killing itself.

Despite its groundling status, the kiwi is a well-qualified

sprinter. It easily outdistances an unmounted man and can hold its own against dogs. Most kiwis that are captured by dogs are surprised during daylight when they are asleep in their burrows.

Although a subject for zoological study for more than a century, the kiwi has been seen in a live state by relatively few ornithologists. Those who have seen the bird at close quarters find the kiwi so ludicrous in appearance that they are moved to attempts at whimsy, even in scientific writings.

The noted New Zealand naturalists F. W. Hutton and James Drummond felt called upon to assert: "Not a bone in its frame or a muscle on its ungainly body, and hardly a feather of its hair-like plumage has escaped minute and elaborate description. Its innermost private life has been invaded; and its habits, its clumsy gait, its wretchedly defenseless condition, its family failings, its deformities and malformations have been made public."

Like a Walt Disney character come to life, the kiwi literally sniffs its way through life, depending on its keen sense of smell to guide it, in compensation for its pitifully weak eyes. To facilitate this, the nostrils are in the very tip of the elongated beak, which comprises nearly one-third of the bird's total length. With audible snorts, the kiwi wobbles ungracefully along, its beak inquisitively probing the ground at each step. Its sense of smell is so acute that it literally smells worms underground before driving its bill into the earth.

The kiwi runs like a novice tightrope walker, placing each foot exactly before the other in a straight line, while its tailless rear sways wildly from side to side in a feathery burlesque of the cancan.

Had it not been for the war, popular interest in the kiwi would probably have remained confined to New Zealand. But before the war ended, every newspaper reader and serviceman knew the gallant New Zealand fighting forces as Kiwis.

There are numerous theories as to how the name Kiwi came to be generally applied to the New Zealanders fighting all over the world. One story says that the term was first applied to them by their Australian neighbors. Another attributes it to the popularity of an English shoe polish using the kiwi as a trademark and brand name. This version has it that Arab servants employed in polishing New Zealand officers' shoes in North Africa began calling them all "Mr. Kiwi."

Regardless of origin, the term quickly gained acceptance and was applied to all New Zealand forces on land, sea, and in the air—much to the disgust of airforcemen, who resented being named after a flightless bird. Soon American and English airmen were calling their own ground crews Kiwis because they did not fly.

When the Pacific battle started, the term was so popular that the New Zealand Third Division on duty against Japan boasted the kiwi as an official insigne. They published a service newspaper entitled "The Kiwi News" and received all their mail and supplies with the kiwi stenciled on the containers. German propaganda leaflets dropped for New Zealand troops in Africa addressed them familiarly, as Kiwis and featured illustrations of the national bird. Military cartoonists habitually used the kiwi to symbolize New Zealand forces.

When New Zealand troops retreated from Greece after a valiant but futile holding operation, they sadly remarked, "We kiwis can't fly, but, by God, we can run."

Today the kiwi is prominent in every aspect of New Zealand life. Its awkward figure graces stamps, bank notes, and coins. Business firms using its name range from the Kiwi Dental Repairs Company to the Kiwi Cake Kitchen. It has been adopted as the distinguishing mark of the New Zealand Manufacturers Federation and appears on all products made by the organization's members.

At least one noteworthy New Zealander, however, takes

issue with all this kiwi-consciousness. He is Arthur P. Harper, President of the Forest and Bird Protection Society of New Zealand.

"America has her eagle that stands for freedom," he says. "Britain has the bulldog to signify tenacity. We've adopted a beastly bird that isn't even good to eat."

Harper, an eighty-four-year-old New Zealand pioneer, ought to know. Credited with opening up large regions of New Zealand through his exploration in the last century, Harper has spent most of his life in the native bush along with the kiwis. In the old days, he ate kiwi on many occasions.

"It tastes terrible," he reports. "Like an old piece of pork boiled in second-hand coffee."

The workers among the Parasol Ants carry large pieces of leaf underground; hence the name. Early naturalists thought that the leaves were to shingle the nest during the tropical rainy season. However, the ants actually grow fungus gardens on them, producing fungus masses as large as cauliflower heads.

(*See page 196.*)

Infant Sea Horses emerging from the father's pouch where
he has brooded them.

(*See page 206.*)

The Kiwi resembles everything but what it actually is. Its wings, naked and useless, are concealed beneath its thick hair-like feathers.

(*See page 214.*)

Schram photo

Photo by Kurt S

FLIPPY, THE EDUCATED PORPOISE

In the climax of Flippy's performance, he tows a surfboard
carrying a girl and a dog. (*See page 225.*)

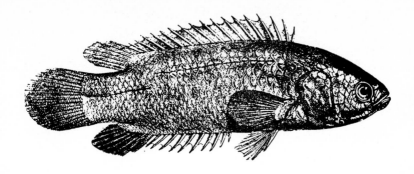

The Walking Fish

A fish that drowns without air. A drawing of *Anabas scandens,*
taken from *The Fishes of India* by Dr. Francis Day. The average
length attained by Anabas is six inches.

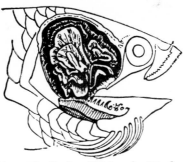

From The Study of Fishes, *by Günther*

The air breathing organ of Anabas. It is this
superbranchial structure, occupying a cavity over
the gills, that enables the fish to absorb atmospheric oxygen.

(*See page 232.*)

Kenneth S. Norris photo

The Fringe-foot's "sand shoe" has fringes of long, flat scales. Forced outward, they increase toe surface on yielding sand.

The Fringe-Footed Sand Lizard is harmless and most interesting to observe. If lucky, you may see it run on its hind legs. (*See page 242.*)

Kenneth S. Norris photo

The Remora appears to swim upside down, but the suction disc is really on the top of the head. The fish at right was photographed while clinging to the glass of a tank.

(*See page 246.*)

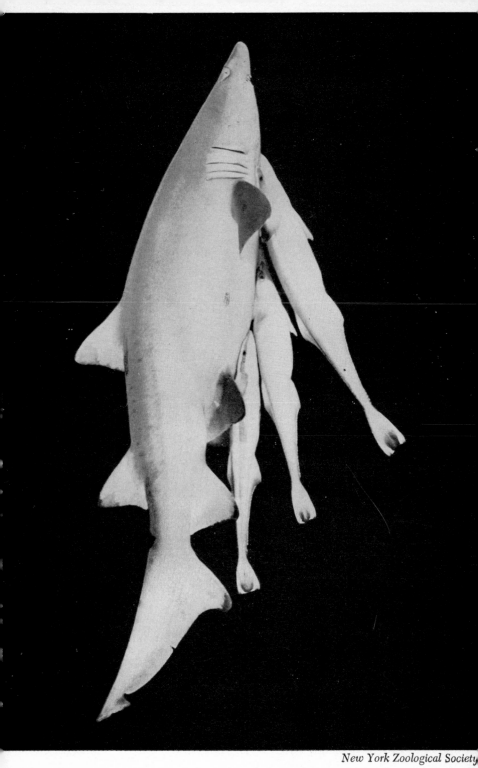

Remoras attached to a Sand Shark. They will share the shark's
meal when he finds it.

THE FIRST EDUCATED PORPOISE *Flippy can ring for his dinner, retrieve sticks, honk a horn, jump through hoops, and tow a surfboard* BY JOHN W. DILLIN.

DISCUSSING the accomplishments of Flippy, the trained porpoise under observation at Marine Studios, Marineland, Florida, someone commented:

"If Flippy gets any smarter, he'll be talking."

To which Adolf Frohn, Flippy's trainer, replied, "He does talk, but we aren't smart enough to understand him."

While Mr. Frohn meant this as a quip, it has foundation in fact. Porpoises are capable of making a wide variety of sounds including jaw clapping, whistling, chirping, squeaking, and the drawn-out grating noise of a rusty hinge. All are made underwater, and some are loud enough to the human ear to be heard at a distance.

Once when a mother and daughter porpoise were separated in the oceanarium of Marine Studios, there were definite signs of communication. They had been temporarily placed in separate tanks with a shallow connecting flume between them. Throughout the separation, the younger animal whistled persistently, and the mother, although she could not see her offspring, frequently answered while remaining close to the gate of the connecting flume.

This and other characteristics of the porpoise suggest the question: Just how much can these fishlike mammals be taught?

In 1947, the late Arthur F. McBride, Curator of Marine Studios, and D. O. Hebb of McGill University and the Yerkes Laboratories of Primate Biology, Orange Park, Florida, collaborated on a study of the behavior of captive porpoises.

Among the problems they considered were ways of determining the relative intelligence of these animals. It was known that the subjects of their investigation, the common bottle-nosed dolphin, or porpoise, *Tursiops truncatus*, has a brain larger than that of a man. It had also been reported that the convolutions of his brain are more marked than in man. But, of course, it cannot be assumed on the basis of these features alone that psychological development is at a corresponding level.[1]

As McBride and Hebb pointed out, the word "intelligence" has never been defined to the satisfaction of everyone, and consequently there are no generally agreed-upon tests or criteria by which the mental capabilities of animals (including man) can be compared and rated. However, at the conclusion of their study they pointed out that the porpoise, so far as certain aspects of his behavior are concerned, appears to fall somewhere in the range of development between the dog and the chimpanzee—in other words, at a rather high level.

Within the past year, further evidence has been obtained to substantiate these findings as the result of a project undertaken at Marineland to determine the extent to which a porpoise can be trained to obey commands. In this respect, at least, Flippy, the animal selected for training, has exceeded all expectations.

Flippy is a member of one of the 22 species of small-toothed whales found along the Atlantic and Pacific coasts of North America. Although properly called dolphins, Flippy and his kind are commonly referred to as porpoises. Bottle-nosed porpoises have been successfully maintained at Marine Studios for a number of years and have even conceived and borne young in their giant oceanarium home. It was only natu-

[1] Actually, one has to consider the relation of brain weight to the animal's total weight. The extent of the convolutions indicates the area of cortex (the outer layer of gray matter) in relation to the rest of the brain. But they may be less important than the *organization* of the cortex, so far as intelligence is concerned. Here the brain of a porpoise and the brain of an ape are quite different, the porpoise apparently lacking the frontal association area.

ral that a member of this species should be selected for what were to prove some very popular experiments.

Flippy had been captured in an inlet by means of a net blocking his escape. Estimated to be about two years old, he weighed approximately 150 pounds and measured close to 6 feet.

His name was suggested by Mrs. Cornelius Vanderbilt Whitney, wife of the Chairman of the Board of Directors of Marine Studios. To anyone who has ever seen a porpoise leaping clear of the water with only a few powerful flips of its tail, the name is quite appropriate.

His first home was a 20-foot tank, which received a constant flow of fresh sea water.

The man selected to conduct the training came from the fourth in that many generations of animal trainers. Adolf Frohn is a native of Germany, and in Europe he had been successful in working with white rats, pigeons, racoons, pigs, pelicans, seals, and sea lions. Prior to coming to Marineland, he had never seen a porpoise. Today he admits he lacked any confidence in teaching a "fish" to do "tricks."

The first step in training an animal is to teach it its source of food. Flippy, like all porpoises, is a fisheater, and he soon learned that Mr. Frohn was the "fishman." First the fish were thrown into the water of the tank. In only one week, Flippy was taking fish from his trainer's hand. The porpoise ate well from the beginning, and achievement came fast as Mr. Frohn gained the mammal's confidence. In three weeks, the porpoise showed almost full trust and accepted food very gently from his trainer's hand.

From this point in the progressive training program, Mr. Frohn has jealously guarded his secrets of just how he has accomplished the final results. It is clear, however, that infinite patience was a prime requisite. His success was complete, as the porpoise itself will demonstrate with his performances.

Here are some of the accomplishments:

On a signal from hand or voice, Flippy has been taught to roll over and over in the water. He will continue to perform until Mr. Frohn ceases to command him.

When the trainer throws a stick onto the surface of the water, the porpoise will swim to it, grasp it in his mouth, swim back to the thrower, and deposit it in his hand.

On instruction, Flippy will swim across the tank and raise his full length out of the water to grasp a rubber ball to which a bell is attached. In doing this, he causes the bell to ring. He then releases it, lowers himself back into the water, and returns to be rewarded. In other words, he rings his own dinner bell.

Mr. Frohn holds in his hand a small horn that is honked by a rubber bulb. Flippy will bite it hard enough to depress the bulb but not hard enough to puncture it. He will repeat the performance as long as his trainer tells him to do so.

The dolphin will swim through a hand-held underwater hoop, turn around and swim through it again and again, as he is instructed.

One of his more interesting accomplishments is to sit halfway out of the water and, on each flick of his trainer's wrist, swim a stroke backward with the upper part of his body well above the surface. Upon reaching a halfway point in the tank, he will stop to await a ball thrown to him. Flippy will catch it in midair and then return it to Mr. Frohn's hand.

Teaching the animal to jump out of the water and hurdle an object required more lengthy schooling. Now he will not only jump through a three-foot hoop suspended three feet above the water, but he will leap through it even with a piece of paper pasted over the hoop.

Evidence of his enjoyment in performing is demonstrated when the animal swims into his own harness. Getting the mammal into his first harness required much time and patience and was one of the most difficult tasks undertaken in the program.

Once the porpoise learned, however, he voluntarily remained quiet until it was fastened:

Transferred to a lagoon after several months of work, Flippy was introduced to two new partners. One was Mr. Frohn's household pet, his fox terrier. In time they were friends.

In the training program, Flippy had his head out of the water so much that he actually became sunburned. As a treatment, Mr. Frohn applied petroleum jelly. Observing the trainer smoothing the jelly over the porpoise's head, the fox terrier offered its own natural treatment. On several occasions, the dog was observed licking Flippy's sunburn, for which the porpoise held still as though enjoying it.

The dog fitted into the training by being towed on an aquaplane by Flippy.

The second partner was a girl. Once accustomed to each other, the girl would enter the water with the porpoise. From Flippy's harness was a rope which she would grasp, and the porpoise would tow her. He later gave her a ride on a surfboard, and sometimes both the dog and the girl would ride behind the porpoise on the board.

In the November, 1949, issue of *Natural History* Magazine, Dr. J. Kenneth Doutt, of the Carnegie Museum of Pittsburgh, gave an account of how a woman was caught in an undertow while swimming. Suddenly she was given a tremendous shove and landed on the beach, face down and exhausted. No person in the water was in sight, but approximately eighteen feet from the shore was a porpoise.

A witness informed the woman that the porpoise had shoved her ashore and, what is more, it was the second time that he had seen a person saved in a like manner.

The editor of *Natural History* pointed out that it would be easy to assume that the air-breathing porpoise was intentionally helping a creature who would drown if deprived of air.

But most students of animal behavior, he noted, will prefer to explain the rescue as a result of the animal's natural curiosity and playfulness.

Whatever the full interpretation, the porpoise's inclination to nose a floating object through the water is given some verification by Mr. Frohn's experience in training Flippy. He used a boat in the lagoon to get from position to position. As he endeavored to paddle, the porpoise would push on the boat and steer it, sometimes on but more often off course.

Incidentally, Mr. Frohn can't swim, yet he spent much of his time in the boat without apparent fear. It might be surmised that he looked upon Flippy as his lifeguard.

During the period of schooling in the lagoon, Mr. Frohn was handing Flippy a fish. Either the porpoise was too affectionate or too eager to receive his food. Nevertheless, Flippy suddenly leaped completely out of the water into the lap of Brother Frohn, who was sitting in the boat. Startled for a moment, the trainer lifted the 200 pounds of wiggling porpoise back into the water.

Just how much further Marine Studios can go to demonstrate Flippy's learning ability, or that of any other porpoise, depends entirely on the ingenuity of the trainer.

All who have seen Flippy perform concede that he is a genuinely smart animal. However, Mr. Frohn says with commendable scientific spirit, "Actually, he may be a dumb one!" As yet he has had no opportunity to compare this particular specimen with other porpoises, since it is the only one with which he has worked.

Another porpoise is on the future program of Marine Studios. It is planned to obtain a female long-snouted dolphin, or spotted porpoise (*Stenella plagiodon*), which is an offshore variety.

In the meantime, Flippy's training continues. He is learning now to pull a lanyard that raises Marineland's porpoise pennant to the top of a mast.

This he might be doing as a symbol of raising the porpoise flag over the marine mammal world on behalf of the many porpoises that have become the favorite pets of the seas and in acknowledgment of the great popular interest that has been accorded these animals at Marine Studios during the past fourteen years.

FISH THAT WALK *Anabas can breathe either air or water, has a homing instinct on land, and is good eating* BY HUGH M. SMITH, FORMERLY FISHERIES ADVISOR TO THE KINGDOM OF SIAM.

IN 1791 a Dane named Daldorff, while in Tranquebar, at that time a Danish possession in India, came upon a fish which, during a heavy rainfall, was climbing a Palmyra palm and had reached a point five feet above the ground. There it was apparently enjoying itself in a little stream running in a fissure in the palm's trunk from a broad frond, which collected the rain water as in a funnel. Near by was a swamp from which the fish had probably come.

Daldorff published his observations in the *Transactions of the Linnaean Society of London* in 1797 and described the fish as a new species under the name of *Perca scandens,* or climbing perch. He was the first European to give an account of the live fish, but the species had already received the name of *testudineus* (in reference to its hard covering like a turtle shell) at the hands of the German zoologist Bloch in 1795, so the significant name applied by Daldorff had to yield to the law of priority.

The name Climbing Perch by which the fish has generally come to be known among English speaking people and in English works of reference is somewhat inappropriate. The fish is not a perch and is not even remotely related to the true perches, common fresh-water fishes of America, Europe, and northern Asia. The generic name *Perca* first borne by the fish had no nomenclatorial standing, and in 1817 the fish was brought by Cuvier under the new generic name *Anabas,* or climber, and became the type of the oriental family Anabantidae, which includes such well known species as the diminu-

tive paradise fish, the Siamese fighting fish, and the giant gor-
amy. All of the members of this family have, in addition to
gills, an accessory breathing apparatus, and most of them
blow bubbles to form a floating nest in which the eggs remain
during incubation.

Alternate common names by which this fish has been called
are Climbing Fish and Walking Fish, but these are borne also
by several gobies, catfishes, serpent-head fishes, etc. On the
whole, it may be best to adopt the perfectly distinctive generic
name as the common designation of the fish in European lan-
guages and call it Anabas.

Anabas seldom exceeds eight inches in length and averages
about six inches when fully adult. Its blunt head is very hard,
and the gill covers are bordered with backwardly projecting
spines. The body is enclosed in a thick, tough coat covered
with hard overlapping scales, which are edged with spinules.
The dorsal and anal fins contain sharp spiny rays. The thick
skin retards the loss of moisture from the tissues when the fish
is out of the water, and the spinous armament discourages or
altogether prevents the attacks of water and land snakes, water
lizards, birds, and other fishes. The small, conical teeth are in
bands in each jaw, and are adapted for crushing insects,
shrimps, and snails, which constitute a large part of the food.

There are gills such as ordinary fishes possess, but the gills
in the long process of evolution have become less important
and are now quite inadequate to sustain life. This is easily
shown by putting a fish in an aquarium with a wire-mesh
screen just below the surface. With inability to take in atmospheric air, the fish begins to suffer and will soon die. The reduced gills represent only a small proportion of the total respiratory surface, and the major part of respiration is carried
on by means of a special structure occupying a cavity over the
gills and consisting of a series of thin, concentrically arranged
bony plates covered by a vascular mucus membrane which
enables the fish to absorb atmospheric oxygen.

Some writers have apparently failed to appreciate the exact role of the accessory branchial organ in Anabas. Thus, Dr. Francis Day, who spent many years in India and Burma and published a monumental work on the fishes of those countries, stated that the

hollow superbranchial organ . . . enables the climbing perch to retain water for a considerable time, so that it can moisten its gills and live whilst out of its native element.

As has already been noted, this organ is dissociated from the gills and enables the fish to breathe atmospheric air when the gills can not be used. The gills function only when the fish is submerged; the superbranchial organ functions only when the fish is out of the water. In this species we have an example of a water animal that is in course of evolution into a land animal, or, perhaps more correctly, a normally water-breathing creature that has already ceased to depend entirely on its gills and ultimately may respire only atmospheric air.

In the Dravidian language of Ceylon and India the name for Anabas means a tree climber, but the tree-climbing powers of the fish have been viewed with doubt or altogether denied by some of the leading ichthyologists of India. Thus, Doctor Day, in his work *The Fishes of Malabar* (1864), refrained from expressing a positive opinion, and said:

The climbing properties attributed to this fish in other portions of India and Ceylon are fully believed in by the inhabitants of Malabar. Certainly it is with difficulty that they can be retained in a vivarium as unless it is covered or [unless] its summit [is] upwards of a foot from the water, they invariably escape. They are able to progress along the ground in two ways, either by lying on their sides, flapping their tails, and moving their pectoral fins, or else chiefly by the aid of the latter fins, first one being advanced and then the other. They can erect their fins and likewise their scales at pleasure, even down to those at the base of the caudal fin. This power of erection, especially as it also exists in the gill covers, would be of great assistance did they employ the latter in climbing.

Dr. Francis Hamilton, in *An Account of the Fishes Found in the River Ganges and Its Branches* (1822), regarded the habit ascribed to this fish by Daldorff as non-existent and held that Daldorff's powers of observation were defective. Thus:

To what enjoyment this dangerous faculty of climbing trees could lead a wretched fish, I am totally at a loss to imagine, and I therefore believe that Daldorff was mistaken; but to what circumstance, neglected to be noticed in his narrative, the error should be attributed, I cannot take upon myself to say.

There is no reason why Anabas should climb trees as a regular habit, and in my rather extensive acquaintance with the fish in India, Burma, Ceylon, Siam, French Indo-China, Malaya, the Philippines, and some of the Indo-Australian islands I have never known one to climb a tree or to be found in a tree except at its base. But from what I know of the out-of-water movements of this fish, I would have no difficulty or hesitation in accepting Daldorff's statement. A Palmyra palm, with its rough bark and its fronds beginning near the ground, would be no more formidable for an Anabas to ascend than would be the vertical side of a wicker basket. For a fish that for weeks or months may have been suffering from a deficiency of water, a stream of rain water flowing down an inclined palm trunk would have a strong appeal.

The climbing powers of Anabas are exercised chiefly in leaving its home in a pond, swamp, or canal and seeking other waters that may afford better living or feeding conditions. In making this change of quarters, the fish may have to travel on dry land, and it is this habit that is characteristic and well known to oriental people. In Siam, I not infrequently came upon an Anabas, usually at night, crossing a dusty road or traversing a lawn or field. It was easy to discover the water a fish was leaving but it was not always possible to determine the particular water to which it was heading. In some cases, the body of water to which the fish was obviously bound did not seem to the human observer to be more attractive than the water it had left. The banks of drying canals and ponds up which the fish has to climb may be high and steep, and skill and patience may be required to negotiate them; but on arriving at a new body of water, the fish may exercise much less care in descending, and I occasionally saw one, apparently deliberately, roll or fall down a steep bank and go into the water with a splash.

As would be expected in a fish that regularly leaves the water and travels overland, Anabas displays no conspicuous color that might attract attention. The adult fish is of a uniform dark brown, while the young is light brown, with a few blackish transverse stripes.

The walking powers of Anabas seem to be exercised only when in quest of a new aquatic environment, and there appear to be no observations indicating that the fish regularly feeds when out of the water, although it may conceivably seize insects or worms that happen to be in its path.

The walking movements lack the grace and ease of those of a lizard and of some of the gobies, such as the mudskipper (*Periophthalmus*). The gait is jerky but comparatively fast, and the efforts are usually persistent, so that a fish may travel a considerable distance in a short time. I have a note on the actually observed out-of-water movements of an Anabas in Peninsular Siam. This fish had been living in a small pool in a detached circular garden thickly planted with flowers and shrubs but was removed when the pool was to be cleaned. It was taken by a servant for release in a stream on the edge of the compound. The servant, however, was called away and put down the basket containing the fish just before reaching the stream. The fish immediately climbed out and, instead of entering the near-by stream, headed back in the direction of the pool. Its subsequent movements were partly conjectured but were under observation during the latter half of the journey. The fish first passed through grass and then over a metalled driveway between houses; and on arriving at the garden, it continued on the driveway to the far side and then made a short turn, plunged through the flower beds, and re-entered the pool. The distance traveled was more than three hundred feet, and the time occupied was about thirty minutes. This particular fish, in addition to progressing readily on dry land and breathing atmospheric air, had well-developed aerial vision (which is rare in fishes) and seemed to exhibit a homing instinct.

Anabas is a valuable food fish in India, Burma, Siam, Malaya, China, and the islands lying off the southeast coast of Asia. Its importance to man arises from the inherent edible quality of its flesh, from the adaptability of the fish to almost any kind of water, and from its hardiness, which permits easy handling in commerce. In Siam it is one of the staple foods over the whole country and is in great repute for its wholesomeness and for its invigorating quality in convalescence. The Siamese name is *pla mor,* or doctor fish. It is taken to market in tubs with little or no water and in wicker baskets, and is usually exposed for sale out of water. It apparently suffers little or no inconvenience from such treatment, its only requirement during a long day in the market being infrequent sprinkling with fresh water to keep its air-breathing apparatus moist.

Various kinds of basket traps and nets are employed in taking Anabas for market; and the fish is much sought and easily caught by youthful anglers using almost any kind of bait on a short line attached to a slender bamboo pole. In many places the children thus keep their families supplied with fresh fish.

Young Siamese fishermen sometimes insert the head of a newly caught Anabas between their teeth so as to leave both hands free to rebait and recast the line, while in India fishermen often kill their catch by putting the fish in their mouths and biting the backbone just behind the head. On rare occasions this practice has led to dire consequences, for the fish has given a jerk, wriggled into the back of the mouth, and become lodged in the pharynx, from which extraction is almost impossible owing to the strong backward-projecting spines on the sides of the head. When in Siam, I learned of several deaths from suffocation when Anabas became tightly impacted over the windpipe of fishermen; and Dr. E. W. Gudger, of the American Museum of Natural History, has published accounts of these and many other cases in which oriental children and adults have been killed by having live fish wedged in the pharynx.

FISH THAT CLIMB TREES ✻ *They actually climb the sloping roots of the mangrove tree* ✻ BY EDWARD WEYER, JR., EDITOR, NATURAL HISTORY MAGAZINE.

IN THE spring of 1945, *Natural History* Magazine received an inquiry about a strange creature that had been seen by a young man stationed in Liberia, Africa. He described his experience as follows, seeking an authoritative opinion about the animal:

"Alighting from the canoe at a native village, we saw things move on the bank. I thought they were lizards, but Wray looked closer and said they were something he had seen in movies taken in Australia. . . . They varied from two to five inches in length and were shaped like a wedge. They had two reddish eyes set on a short stem above the head and two limbs more like fins than anything else, just behind the head. They used these as legs and hopped toad-fashion or crawled slowly. We couldn't catch any, because they all moved under the bank or into the water, but they wouldn't stay in the water long. We saw them quite close up, and Wray is sure they look like what he saw in the movies. Maybe you can find out for me what they are and what they are called. . . ."

We were able to ascertain from the American Museum's Department of Fishes and Aquatic Biology that this creature was almost surely the Mudskipper, a fish famous for leaving the water and walking or hopping about on sand or mud in pursuit of food. It is found in tropical waters in the eastern Atlantic (West Africa) and the Indo-Pacific. The examples described by our correspondent in Liberia were probably *Periophthalmus koelrenteri* (Pallas).

J. R. Norman, in his *A History of Fishes,* wrote that this fish "chases its insect prey among weeds and rocks, and on land is quite as agile as many lizards. The pectoral fins are specially modified in relation to this habit, each being attached at the end of a kind of muscular arm, which can be moved backwards and forwards and is used exactly like a limb. Among other structural peculiarities designed to assist its progression on land, the low anal fin and the stout lower rays of the caudal may be noticed. Dr. Regan writes: 'When walking on the mud each step is accomplished by a forward movement of both pectoral fins, which are then put on the ground and draw the rest of the body after them; these steps are repeated rapidly, and as each results in an advance of about half an inch, very fair progress is made; the pelvic fins support the body during the turning forward of the pectorals. But, as their name implies, the Mudskippers often leap along the mud, or from one stone to another; short jumps may be accomplished by the action of the pectoral fins alone, but longer ones, which may be as much as a yard long, are made by a stroke of the tail. This is their way of getting along when they are in a hurry, and they may often be seen playing on the mud, jumping about in chase of each other.' "

A remarkable photograph of a Mudskipper was among the many interesting things brought back by the late Martin Johnson from Borneo in 1936. The fish is shown well up on the sloping root of a mangrove tree, where it has worked its way by action of its forward fins. Such a position is described as a favorite aerial retreat of the fish.

When not tree-climbing, the Mudskipper enjoys long periods of repose at the water's edge with only its tail submerged. Second only to its walking and climbing ability is the fact that it "breathes" more efficiently through its tail fin than by means of its gills. Tests prove that it can survive for a day and a half with only its tail submerged, while if only the gills are allowed to function, it lives but 12 to 18 hours.

When alarmed, the Mudskipper springs by means of its

bent, muscular fins and then skims across the water to safety by a succession of short jumps.

Note the movable, bulbous eyes, which excel the eyes of ordinary fishes in being adjustable to vision in the air. Without them, this fish would see no more distinctly out of water than a person can see in it. But a specially developed muscle enables the climbing-fish to shift the spherical lens of its eye so close to the retina as to produce a sharp image, even of objects not in its immediate vicinity.

Its remarkable eyes and its respiratory tail fin make this fish a scientific curiosity and an object of wonderment to all who have witnessed its tree-climbing, tail-breathing activities.

❧ SAND SWIMMER ❧ *The Fringe-footed Sand Lizard swims and dives in the desert sands* ❧ BY KENNETH S. NORRIS.

To most people, deserts imply heat and desolation—a stark world of barren mountains and forbidding sand dunes. The only living things seen by a casual visitor are the few small plants that seem half buried in the sand valleys. The surrounding sand hills stand ready to engulf even these few evidences of life. In sand dune areas a hawk may be seen soaring overhead or an occasional small bird flitting among the scattered bushes, but more likely no living animal will be noted on the dunes themselves.

But closer observation of the sandy wastes of our Southwestern deserts will reveal numerous tracks in places not swept smooth by the winds. These indicate that many animals dwell in an area where the visitor least expects to find them.

As you walk between the dunes, you may see a puff of sand 100 yards away, as a small creature, running at high speed, disappears around the end of a dune. This excessively wary animal is Uma, the Fringe-footed Sand Lizard; and usually you will see no more of it than this first puff of sand. But if you follow the lizard's tracks, you will find that they stop abruptly on the slope of the dune. Place your fingers in the sand above this last track and rake down the dune face. The instant you touch the wily little creature you must grasp it or it will burst from the sand and be off, running on its hind legs and only occasionally touching its front feet to the sand for balance. When you capture Uma by this method, be careful not to pick up a resting sidewinder, for this small rattlesnake is often found partially buried in the sand.

Uma's method of burrowing is called "sand swimming."

The creature dives into the sand, often while running at full speed, with its front legs pressed against its flanks. Lateral undulatory movements of the body and movements of the hind legs drive the animal into the sand; and rapid vibrations of the tail finally sink it completely. Most "swims" are short.

Sand swimming has added a third dimension to Uma's world, for the lizard is not restricted to living on the surface. Uma is remarkably adapted in several ways to its burrowing habits. Its tail and body are flattened, giving the animal a thin appearance when viewed from the side. The head is wedge-shaped and perfectly adapted for entering soft sand at high speeds.

Most animals without Uma's protective devices would find dune life rigorous because of wind-blown sand entering their eyes, ears, and nostrils. But Uma's eyes are protected by a series of scales called lappets, which fringe the edges of the eyelids. Under the sand, these are tightly pressed together, preventing the entrance of sand grains. Should sand enter, the grains become moistened and are rolled into a small pellet by movements of the eyes. A blood sinus in the corner of the eye becomes filled with blood and distends the nictitating membrane (present in man as the little knob in the corner of the eye) and thus forces the sand pellet outward. Uma removes the pellet with the toes of its hind feet, which are modified for this action. The nails are flattened, and only the flat side touches the eye, so the delicate eye surface is not scratched.

The nostrils can be closed against the entrance of sand by "valves," which may even permit limited breathing while the animal is beneath the surface.

A short hike through the dunes will be enough to convince most people that locomotion over soft sand is extremely difficult. Yet Uma attains speeds that are remarkable. One time, while driving over a nearly level area of deep sand in a four-wheel-drive truck, a large Uma was frightened from hiding and ran in front of the vehicle. It was all I could do to keep abreast of the swift creature. My speedometer showed that this five-inch lizard was running at fifteen miles an hour. At the end of the chase, I was able to pick up the exhausted animal by hand. Uma can run up 35-degree sand dune slopes at such speed that when the sharp crest is reached, you may see the creature shoot several inches into the air.

Uma's common name, Fringe-footed Sand Lizard, is taken from one of the structures adapting the animal for locomotion on sand. On its toes it wears "sand shoes," consisting of long, flat, pointed scales. When Uma runs, these fringes are forced outward and increase the toe surface, thus giving the animal better footing. Some of the toes of the hind feet are extremely long and serve to distribute the animal's weight over a large area, thereby preventing it from sinking into the soft sand.

In the dune areas, the smooth open stretches offer few places where an animal may forage in safety. Overhead, several species of hawks patrol the dunes for food, scanning the terrain with their amazingly acute eyes. On the sand, foxes, badgers, and snakes search for prey. Uma lives almost exclusively upon insects and has no weapons with which to combat these predators. Instead, it relies upon its fleetness, its sand swimming, and its protective coloration. The latter is truly remarkable. The color and pattern of the animal combine to make it all but invisible on the dunes. Nearly white Umas live in white dunes, and those living in rusty-red sand are so nearly the same color that it is virtually impossible to see them until they move.

Much remains to be learned about Uma. One of its more perplexing features is the parietal eye. Just behind the level of the eyes, on the top of the lizard's head, is an enlarged scale, called the interparietal scale. In the center of this is a clear lenslike structure. Microscopic examination of this structure shows that it has many of the features of a true eye, such as a lens, fluid cavity, rod cells, and a retinal layer. The function of the parietal eye is unknown. Apparently it is sightless, and it has not been conclusively demonstrated that any nerve connections lead to it.

The notion that deserts are hot is often though not always true. The pursuit of desert animals during the day can be most uncomfortable and sometimes dangerous because of extreme heat. However, a little hunting on the dunes will show that lizards and most other animals do not stay in the sun but retreat underground during the hottest parts of the day. This is not at all surprising when one considers that when air temperatures reach 115 degrees F. at the height of a man's shoulders, the sand surface upon which Uma lives may reach 189 degrees. The lizard remains active and above the surface only so long as there are temperatures that happen also to be reasonably comfortable for man.

HITCHHIKER OF THE SEA *Free rides and free meals reward the surprising remora* BY N. J. BERRILL, OF MCGILL UNIVERSITY.

WHEN Columbus returned to the Caribbean the year after his first voyage of discovery, he was in less of a hurry to get back to Spain and took more time to explore. He found Cuba to be a lovely island, and it was during a leisurely voyage among the islets off the south coast, which he called the Gardens of the Queen, that Indians came in a canoe to hunt turtles with a fish.

The Admiral himself watched while they fastened a cord to the tail of a curious fish and let it go down into the sea with the line held to the canoe. The explorers who were with him recorded their observations as follows: These fish "have a large mouth all full of suckers like a cuttlefish, and they are very daring, as ferrets are here. And when they are thrown into the water, they go to fasten themselves on some fish; of these they do not leave hold in the water but only when they are pulled out . . . they had one of these fish fastened on the bottom of a large turtle, and they waited to get it into the canoe." The description is not quite accurate, for the suckers are not in the mouth but on the top of the head. And while Columbus was not familiar with the fish, it is one that was well known to the ancient civilizations of the Mediterranean.

The fish was the remora (pronounced REM-o-ra), otherwise known as the Shark-sucker. Its peculiarity is that its dorsal fin, which starts life like the dorsal fin of most other fishes, changes into a complex sucker or adhesive organ shaped like the sole of a shoe and divided into many compartments. The fish uses the sucker to hitchhike from one place to another. By means of suction it attaches itself to any convenient large swimmer of the seas, whether it be a shark, turtle, porpoise, or even the manatee, which Columbus called the mermaid. This is pure laziness, for what the remora gets is a free ride to a free meal. It attaches by the back of its head to the lower side of its traveling companion and hangs on till the meal is reached. Then it drops off long enough to join in the feast, after which it reattaches and goes for another ride. And there is little doubt that the hull of a ship looks as good to the remora as the belly of a shark.

There is a very old legend that the remora can slow down sailing vessels and even stop them altogether. We repeatedly find the idea in medieval and classical literature, and the fish was often drawn on Greek and Roman vases. In fact, the death of the Emperor Caligula was attributed indirectly to a remora, which was supposed to have fastened to his great galley and held it back while the rest of his fleet escaped. Its scientific name, *Echeneis*, itself means "holding back," and older writers usually referred to it as the Ship-holder. The remora is never big enough to exert much force against a moving boat. One kind reaches a length of about sixteen inches, and another about three feet. There is little doubt, however, that a rowboat or small sailboat would be slowed down by one of these underwater hitchhikers, and several of them might make their presence known to the oarsmen of a larger boat. Marc Antony's delay and defeat at the battle of Actium was also supposed to have been caused by the attachment of many suckerfish to his galleys. Perhaps any excuse was better than none, especially when Cleopatra may have been the real reason.

The remora fastens itself very tightly. It has been reported, for example, that when one is attached to the glass of an aquarium, it will hold so firmly that the sucker is left attached to the glass and the fish is so injured that it dies.

Another old name for the suckerfish is the "Reversus," from the mistaken idea that the fish swims on its back. It does give that impression, but it actually swims in the normal manner.

According to reports left by Columbus and his companions, the Caribbean Indians caught these curious fish when they were young and raised them in pools. Before and after a hunting trip below the sea, the Indians would talk to the fish, cajoling and praising them as though they could understand.

There is something very strange in the widespread use of this method of fishing. It reflects either the wanderings of mankind or the tendency of men throughout the ages to use their ingenuity in every possible way to obtain food beyond their reach. There is no doubt that man is inherently lazy and will make someone work for him if he can. But is it not surprising that the remora is employed to hunt fishes, turtles, and other sea animals, with a cord fastened to its tail, not just in the West Indies but in Malaya, China, the Spice Islands, and northeastern Australia? Chinese, Polynesians, Melanesians, and Australian aborigines isolated from the rest of the world for thousands of years, as well as Carib and Lucayan Indians of the West Indies, all use or have used the same fish in the same way. It does seem more reasonable to believe that the statement "Great minds think alike" accounts for this widespread practice, rather than that the method was discovered only once and was then carried over so large a part of the world.

The aborigines of the Barrier Reef angle for suckerfish with hooks made from pearl shell or bone fastened to woven bark lines. Then they fasten the fish by the tail and keep it in shallow water until it is time to hunt for turtles. In leashing the fish, a hole is made at the base of the tail fin by means of a turtle bone, and one end of a very long piece of string is inserted and made fast to the tail. A short piece of string is also passed through the mouth and out the gills, securing the head end, and the fish is slung over the side of the canoe. When a turtle is sighted, the short piece is pulled out of the mouth, and away the remora goes. As a rule, just before the fish is released, the disc and shoulders of the sucker are scrubbed with dry sand to remove the slime and excite the fish.

So long as the line is kept taut, the remora cannot let go of anything it has caught, and the size of the turtle or fish that can be captured is limited only by the strength of the line and the breaking strain of the remora itself. Turtles up to 100 pounds have been hauled to the surface in this way. But when the turtle is very large and clings to the bottom (and green turtles can weigh several hundredweight!), the natives dive overboard and follow the line down to the turtle to secure it with a rope.

One little difference stands out between the customs of the aborigines of Australia and the gentle Indians described by Columbus. Whereas the Indians endowed the remora with intelligent understanding and treated the fish humanely, the Australian aborigines at the end of a day's fishing eat the remora, too.

INDEX

251